Level D

Exploring English
Language Connections and Conventions

Lead Author
Joan Hardy

Contributing Authors
Rosanne Werges, Irene Elmer,
Debbie Diller

ISBN 0-8454-2107-7
©1995 The Continental Press, Inc.

No part of this publication may be reproduced in any form or by any means,
electronic, mechanical, photocopying, recording, or otherwise, without the prior written
permission of the publisher. All rights reserved. Printed in the United States of America.

Continental Press
520 East Bainbridge Street
Elizabethtown, PA 17022

Exploring English
Language Connections and Conventions

Cover Design: Kevin Tufarolo

Interior Design: Pat Gavett and Marcy J. Wilson

Illustrators: Jeani Brunnick, pages 13, 19, 27, 42, 55, 60, 67, 76, 86, 90, 94, 104, 112, and 124; Ray Burns, pages 6, 9, 14, 21, 34, 39, 41, 44, 56, 63, 72, 83, 89, 101, 107, 116, and 120; Yvonne Cherbak, pages 15, 33, 50, 58, 73, 77, 87, 103, 119, and 121; Jim McConnell, pages 8, 32, 38, 48, 54, 69, 75, 95, and 110; Pauline Phung, pages 11, 29, 52, 65, 74, 85, and 108; Don Sibley, pages 16, 22, 40, 57, 68, 79, 100, 106, and 118; Carlin Verreaux, pages 7, 18, 30, 35, 53, 64, 84, 98, 105, and 117.

Project Consultants: Faye Baskauskas, Classroom Teacher
Martinez, California

Debbie Diller, Educational Consultant
Houston, Texas

Myrna T. Walters, Elementary Reading and
Language Arts Coordinator
Seminole, Florida

Marjorie Zucker, Assistant Principal
Brooklyn, New York

CONTENTS

A Note for You

What is the purpose of language? You **speak** and **write** to tell other people what you are thinking. You **listen** and **read** to find out what other people have to say. You **communicate.**

You already know how to do these things. So why should you **study** language? Every language has its own **rules.** When people use the rules, they can understand one another better.

Here's an example. Can you understand this group of words?

Mary said Jim I bet you can't guess what this
means you win Mary said Jim

That looks like nonsense, doesn't it? But if you follow the rules for writing English, the words make sense:

Mary said, "Jim, I bet you can't guess what this
means."
"You win, Mary," said Jim.

This book is called *Exploring English.* It can teach you some of the rules of our language and how to use them when you write.

ABOUT WRITTEN LANGUAGE

How do you **communicate** with other people? You use **language.** You put **words** together to form **sentences** to explain your thoughts.

Think About How many different ways do you use language? Do you make telephone calls? Send birthday cards? Watch TV? Read books? List eight ways that you use language.

_____   _____

_____   _____

_____   _____

_____   _____

Look at your list. Underline the ways you listen to or say language out loud. Circle the ways you read or write language.

These uses for language are alike in some ways. In both, you put **words** together to form **sentences** to explain your thoughts. But when you speak, you sometimes say part-sentences like "Because" or "Maybe." Your listener can tell what you mean from the conversation that has gone before. When you write, you need to use **complete sentences.** Why?

_____

_____

You want your reader to understand what you write, and you won't be there to explain.

Remember A **sentence** is a group of words that tells a **complete thought.** If the words do not tell a complete thought, they are a **fragment.**

Examples   SENTENCE ▶   Deer eat leaves and berries.
FRAGMENT ▶   Eat leaves and berries.
SENTENCE ▶   Too many deer in one place can harm plants.
FRAGMENT ▶   Too many deer in one place.

Think About Read the examples again. Look at both sentences. Then look at the fragments. What is the difference between them?

_____

_____

_____

Apply Read each group of words. Write **S** above each sentence. Write **F** above each fragment.

Large packs of hungry wolves. Wolves often eat deer. Yet wolves are

not harmful to deer herds. Only the sick and weak deer. Without wolves,

deer herds would become too large. Couldn't find enough leaves and

berries. Many deer would starve. Better off with wolves around. These

animal "enemies" actually help one another. Wolves and deer.

Apply Find each group of words that you marked **F** for fragment. Add words to the group to make it a sentence that tells a complete thought.

Remember To tell a complete thought, a sentence needs two parts. The **subject part** tells **who** or **what** the sentence is about.

Examples <u>A warm, sandy beach</u> is interesting.
<u>We</u> always have fun there.

Think About Read the examples again. How are the subject parts alike?

_____

_____

_____

Apply Read the sentences. Underline the subject part in each one.

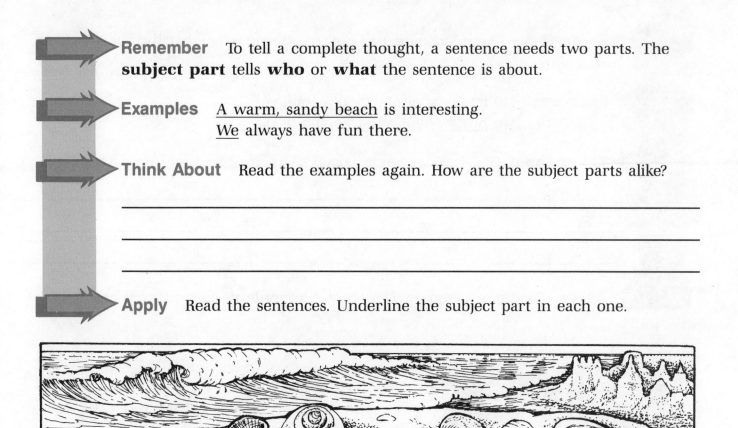

Large, powerful waves crash on the beach. Many colorful shells are brought in by the waves. Tiny animals lived in the shells at one time. Smelly brown plants wash onto the shore, too. Birds with long beaks dig among them for food.

People make sand castles sometimes. A pail and shovel are useful for the task. The best castles win prizes at some beaches.

Apply Write some sentences of your own. Tell what you would like to do at the beach. Then underline the subject part in each of your sentences.

_____

_____

_____

_____

_____

_____

Remember   The **predicate part** of a sentence tells what the subject **does** or **is.**

Examples   My family <u>is crazy about camping</u>.
We <u>bring a tent and sleeping bags</u>.

Think About   Read the examples again. How are the predicate parts alike?

_____

_____

_____

Apply   Read the sentences. Underline the predicate part in each one.

Our favorite places are deep in the woods. Wild animals live nearby. We watch out for bears all the time. Bears are not usually dangerous. They steal food, however. Bears break into tents and cars for tasty treats. We hang our food in bags high up in a tree. Only raccoons can reach it there.

Apply   Write some sentences of your own. Tell what animals you might see in the woods. Then underline the predicate part in each of your sentences.

_____

_____

_____

_____

_____

_____

REVIEW TIME

- ✔ You write a **sentence** to tell a **complete thought**.
- ✔ You tell **who** or **what** the sentence is about in the **subject part**.
- ✔ You tell what the subject **does** or **is** in the **predicate part**.

Checking your work to try to make it better is called **proofreading.** You can use proofreading marks to show where things should be corrected or changed. You use the mark ∧ where you want to add something. Then you write the new words above the line.

Proofread this story. Add a subject or a predicate to complete each fragment. Use words from the boxes or think of your own words.

SUBJECTS	PREDICATES
Anne Frank The Nazis Their Dutch neighbors But her diary	wrote in her diary had to go into hiding tried to kill all the Jews died when she was only 13

was a Jewish girl who lived in Holland. During World

War II, the Nazis   . Anne and her family   .   helped

them. Every day, Anne   .   finally captured Anne and her

family. Anne Frank   .   became a famous book.

9

THE BUILDING BLOCKS

When you speak or write, you put words together in sentences. You need **different kinds of words** to do the job.

Think About   What do you talk or write about? People? Places? List four things here.

_____

_____

_____

_____

What do you say about these people and things? In front of each of your words, write another word to describe what that person or thing is like.

Do you ever talk or write about doing things? List four things that you like to do.

_____

_____

_____

_____

How do you do these things? After each of your words, write another word to describe the way you do it.

You just listed four different kinds of words. How can they help you communicate?

_____

_____

_____

Different kinds of words tell different kinds of information. Using the different kinds of words lets you say <u>exactly</u> what you mean.

Remember   A **noun** is a **naming** word.

Examples   explorer   hospital   eagle   fern
              cousins   canyons   buffalo   puppets
              Coretta King   Ohio   Lassie   *Silver Streak*

Think About   Read the examples again. What different kinds of things do nouns name?

_____

_____

Apply   Read the sentences. Underline each noun.

The coelacanth is a very special fish. It has lungs and fat, bony fins.

Scientists thought these animals had died out. Then some men caught a

strange creature in their nets. It was off the coast of Africa. The boss of a

nearby museum was called in. Soon the experts had to change their ideas.

After 60 million years, the coelacanth was still around.

Apply   Do some writing of your own. Tell about some animals that really did die out. Then circle each noun in your sentences.

_____

_____

_____

_____

_____

Remember A **singular noun** names **one**. A **plural noun** names **more than one**.

Examples SINGULAR ► child   church   pony   desk
PLURAL ► children   churches   ponies   desks

Think About Read the examples again. What differences do you see between the singular and plural nouns?

_____

Apply Read the sentences. Underline each singular noun. Circle each plural noun.

Parchment is a special kind of paper. Long ago, people in Asia Minor used it. This material was made from the skins of sheep, cows, and goats. First, the fur and fat were removed. Then, the hides were rubbed with stones and chalk. Finally, they could be written on with brushes and ink.

Remember A **common noun** names **any** person, place, animal, or thing. A **proper noun** names a **particular** person, place, animal, or thing.

Examples COMMON ► singer   country   whale   day
PROPER ► Cher   China   Kiko   Monday

Think About Read the examples again. In what way are common and proper nouns written differently?

_____

Apply Read the sentences. Underline each common noun. Circle each proper noun.

Angel Cordero rides racehorses. He has won 11 awards at the racetrack in Saratoga. One year in August, he won four races on the same day. First, the jockey rode Bloomquist Beauty and Crafty Belle. Then he rode Active Wear and George the Boss. Only Manuel Ycaza has won more events here.

Remember   A **possessive noun** names **who or what has something.** It shows ownership.

Examples   NOUN ►   friend   girls
                    POSSESSIVE ►   <u>friend's</u> house   <u>girls'</u> books

Think About   Read the examples again. How are possessive nouns different from regular nouns?

_____

_____

Apply   Read the sentences. Underline each possessive noun.

Animals' bodies are perfectly fitted for their uses. A duck's feathers keep out water. Beavers' tails are flat for slapping the mud. A frog's skin is green so that the animal can hide in the grass. To protect them from cold weather, sheep's wool is thick. A snake's eyes have a covering to keep out dirt. People's bodies are also well designed. Just think of how many things a person's thumb does.

Apply   Do some writing of your own. Think of other animals you have seen. Tell how they are special.

_____

_____

_____

_____

_____

Examples   chop   grumbles   think   buzzed

Think About   Read the examples again. Does a word have to name a movement to be an action verb? Explain your answer.

_____

_____

Apply   Read the sentences. Underline each action verb.

A Greek legend tells how Jason searched for the Golden Fleece. This magic sheepskin hung on a tree in a faraway land. A fierce dragon guarded it. Jason sailed across the sea in his ship, the *Argo*. He took 50 men with him, and they met with many adventures. Jason almost died before he found the Golden Fleece. He stole it from the dragon. The Princess Medea helped him. Then the dragon chased them, but at the very last minute they both escaped.

Apply   Do some writing of your own. Tell about a time you looked and looked for something. Then circle each action verb in your sentences.

_____

_____

_____

_____

_____

Remember A **linking verb** connects the **subject** of the sentence to words in the **predicate.** It tells what the subject **is** or **was.**

Examples
am	was	become	seem
is	were	became	feel
are			

Think About Read the examples again. Which two words do not tell about **being** something?

_____

Apply Read the sentences. Underline each linking verb.

It was winter. People were sad. What was the problem?

For a long time, doctors were no help.

Now scientists are ready with some answers. In winter,

the days are shorter, and there is less sunlight. Without

sunlight, people become unhappy. As soon as summer is here,

they feel better.

Apply Do some writing of your own. Tell about how you feel during the winter. Then circle each linking verb in your sentences.

_____

_____

_____

_____

_____

_____

Remember   Sometimes a **helping verb** comes **before** the **main verb** in a sentence. It helps the main verb to tell about doing or being. Together, the two verbs are called a **verb phrase.**

Examples   HELPING VERB ▼ ▼ MAIN VERB

These pine trees <u>will</u> <u>be</u> green all year.
Their needles <u>have</u> <u>fallen</u> a few at a time.
New ones <u>are</u> <u>growing</u> every day.

Think About   Read the examples again. Look at the verbs **will, have,** and **are.** Are these words always helping verbs?

_____

Apply   Read the sentences. Underline each verb phrase. Circle each helping verb.

For over 800 years there have been llamas in Peru. A cousin of the camel, a llama will carry heavy loads. The llama has helped many people in the mountains. Now campers are using llamas as pack animals. Sometimes angry llamas will spit at people. But usually a llama will be friendly. Many people are buying llamas as pets. The llama has found a new home in this country.

Apply   Do some writing of your own. Tell about an unusual pet you have seen. Then underline each helping verb and circle each main verb.

_____

_____

_____

_____

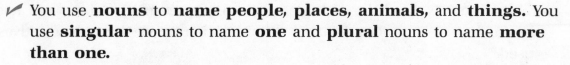

REVIEW TIME

✔ You use **nouns** to **name people, places, animals,** and **things.** You use **singular** nouns to name **one** and **plural** nouns to name **more than one.**

✔ You use **common** nouns to name **general** things and **proper** nouns to name **particular** things.

✔ You use **possessive** nouns to show **ownership.**

✔ You use **verbs** to tell what someone or something **does** or **is.** You use **action** verbs to name **actions, linking** verbs to **connect** the subject with words in the predicate, and **helping** verbs to **help** the main verb do its job.

When you proofread, you use special marks.

∧ means "Add here."

Use this proofreading mark to add nouns and verbs to the report below. Use words from the boxes or think of your own words.

NOUNS		VERBS	
city	people	has grown	knows
Mexico	Today's	disappeared	was

The Mayans lived in   more than 2,000 years ago. They built a

beautiful   called El Mirador. It   very large. The buildings

covered six square miles. At least 10,000   lived there. Then

suddenly they   .

No one   what happened to the Mayans. The jungle   thick

over their huge buildings.   visitors can only wonder what these

ancient people were like.

Remember An **adjective** is a word that **describes a noun.** It tells **what kind, how many,** or **which one.**

Examples The <u>yellow</u> canary flew away.
The eagle was <u>hungry</u>.

Think About Read the examples again. Draw an arrow from each adjective to the noun it describes. What is different about how the two adjectives are used?

_____

_____

Apply Read the sentences. Underline each adjective. Then draw an arrow from the adjective to the noun it describes.

Jade is beautiful and rare. To ancient Chinese, jade was precious. They made sharp tools and scary masks out of it. People like its deep color. The shiny stone can be white, green, or red. Today jade is used to make fine jewelry.

Remember An **article** is a special kind of **adjective.** It signals that a noun will follow. There are three articles: **a, an,** and **the.**

Examples <u>The</u> fly orchid looks like <u>an</u> insect.
It is <u>a</u> small flower.

Think About Read the examples again. Where does an article always come?

_____

Apply Read the sentences. Underline each article.

Each state has a special flower as its symbol. Can you name the official flower of your state? If you are an Alaskan, it's the forget-me-not. If you are from the state of Tennessee, it's an iris. Are you a native of Arizona? An Arizonan's flower is a saguaro cactus blossom.

18

Remember   An **adverb** is a word that **describes an action verb.**

Examples   Aim <u>carefully</u> with your camera.
<u>Now</u> press the button.
Use a flashbulb <u>indoors</u>.

Think About   Read the examples again. What does **carefully** tell about **aim?**

_____ What does **now** tell about **press?** _____

What does **indoors** tell about **use?** _____

Apply   Read the sentences. Underline the adverb in each one. Above the adverb, write HOW, WHEN, or WHERE to explain what it tells about the verb.

Margaret Bourke-White traveled everywhere. She often won awards for her photographs. Margaret handled her camera carefully. She snapped each shot quickly. Later she developed her pictures.

A war started in Europe, so Margaret went there. Soon she had a job with _Life_ magazine. Many people greatly admired her work.

Apply   Do some writing of your own. Tell about some photographs you have taken or seen. Use adverbs that tell how, when, and where.

_____

_____

_____

_____

_____

_____

Remember   A **pronoun** is a word that **takes the place of a noun. Subject pronouns** are used in the **subject part** of a sentence.

Examples   SINGULAR ►   I   you   he, she, it
            PLURAL ►   we   you   they

Think About   Read the examples again. Which pronouns can take the place of nouns that name people? Which can take the place of nouns that name animals, places, or things?

_____

Apply   Read the sentences. Write a pronoun from the examples to complete each one.

Do _____ know any Hopi Indians? Well, _____ do. When

Mom and I were in Arizona, _____ visited a Hopi village. _____

was right out in the desert. Mom knows some Hopi silversmiths.

_____ loves their work. _____ made Mom a special ring. It

shows an ancient god. _____ looks so fierce because his job is to

protect her.

Remember   An **object pronoun** is used after an **action verb** and after a word like **to, of, by, with,** and **from.**

Examples   SINGULAR ►   me   you   him, her, it
            PLURAL ►   us   you   them

Think About   Read the examples again. Which object pronouns are also subject pronouns?

_____

Apply   Read the sentences. Write a pronoun from the examples to complete each one.

Mom and I took the ring home with _____ . Later, Mom told

_____ about the bear god. Sick people call _____ . He comes and

cures _____ . Mom says that's what the Hopi silversmiths told _____ .

Does that sound strange to _____ ? Mom says it might work if you

believed _____ .

Remember A **possessive pronoun** tells **who or what has something.** It shows ownership.

Examples
SINGULAR ► my your his, her, its
PLURAL ► our your their

Think About Read the examples again. Which pronoun can be singular or plural?

_____

Apply Read the sentences. Write a pronoun from the examples to complete each one.

We have students from five different continents in _____ class. Anita moved here with _____ family from Colombia, which is in South America. Vince was born here, but _____ father was born in Italy, a European country. The Phung twins came to live with _____ aunt after the Vietnam War. I know _____ ancestors were Africans, maybe from Gambia. Each country has _____ own interesting customs. Do you know which land _____ family came from?

Apply Do some writing of your own. Tell about your relatives and where they came from. Then circle each pronoun in your sentences.

_____

_____

_____

_____

_____

21

REVIEW TIME

- ✔ You use **adjectives** to **describe nouns.** They tell what kind, how many, or which one. You use special adjectives called **articles** to signal that a noun will follow. The articles are **a, an,** and **the.**

- ✔ You use **adverbs** to **describe action verbs.** They tell how, when, or where.

- ✔ You use **pronouns** to **take the place of nouns.** You use **subject** pronouns as sentence subjects. You use **object** pronouns after action verbs and after words like **to, of, by, with,** and **from.** You use **possessive** pronouns to show ownership.

When you proofread, you use special marks.

∧ means "Add here."

Use this proofreading mark to add adjectives, adverbs, and pronouns to the report below. Use words from the boxes or think of your own.

ADJECTIVES	ADVERBS	PRONOUNS
many	hard	His
deaf	deeply	It
important	directly	us

Alexander Graham Bell cared   about

the   problems of   children. He

worked   to learn everything about human

speech.   long training ended up helping

all of   .   led   to a

very   invention—the telephone.

22

WRITING TIME

A **photo essay** reports information using pictures and captions. *Captions* are sentences that describe or give facts about the pictures.

Write a photo essay about yourself. Collect three or more pictures of yourself. Make some notes about them in the space below.

	People	**Places**
Picture #1 Nouns:	_____	_____
Adjectives:	_____	_____
Picture #2 Nouns:	_____	_____
Adjectives:	_____	_____
Picture #3 Nouns:	_____	_____
Adjectives:	_____	_____

Write several sentences describing each picture. When you describe the people, tell who they are and why they are important. When you describe the places, tell where they are and what you were doing there. Write on another piece of paper.

Follow these steps to write your captions.

1. Use scratch paper for your first copy. Write all the captions you will use.

2. Show your writing to a friend. Talk about how to make it better.

3. Revise your photo essay. Take out things you don't like and add new things. Be sure to use adjectives and adverbs to make your writing interesting.

4. Now proofread your work. Check your spelling and the way you used words.

5. Fasten your photos to some paper. Then copy your corrected captions neatly below each one. Display your work for friends to see.

TEST TIME

Directions Read each sentence. Find the **noun** in it. Then fill in the circle that has the same letter as your answer.	**Sample** The child was hungry. A B C D

Answer Column
S Ⓐ ⬤ Ⓒ Ⓓ

1 Chicago is very large.
   A   B   C   D

4 The sandy beach was warm.
   E   F   G   H

2 Where is Albert now?
   E   F   G   H

5 Heavy storms are scary.
   A   B   C   D

3 The lazy cat slept.
   A   B   C   D

6 The long train stopped.
   E   F   G   H

Answer Column
1 Ⓐ Ⓑ Ⓒ Ⓓ
2 Ⓔ Ⓕ Ⓖ Ⓗ
3 Ⓐ Ⓑ Ⓒ Ⓓ
4 Ⓔ Ⓕ Ⓖ Ⓗ
5 Ⓐ Ⓑ Ⓒ Ⓓ
6 Ⓔ Ⓕ Ⓖ Ⓗ

Directions Read each sentence. Find the **verb** in it. Then fill in the circle that has the same letter as your answer.

Sample
The insect buzzed loudly.
A   B   C   D

Answer Column
S Ⓐ Ⓑ ⬤ Ⓓ

1 My brother was tired.
   A   B   C   D

4 Squirrels scampered up a tree.
   E   F   G   H

2 Marlis won the race.
   E   F   G   H

5 My favorite color is purple.
   A   B   C   D

3 I dropped my glass.
   A   B   C   D

6 Write me a letter soon.
   E   F   G   H

Answer Column
1 Ⓐ Ⓑ Ⓒ Ⓓ
2 Ⓔ Ⓕ Ⓖ Ⓗ
3 Ⓐ Ⓑ Ⓒ Ⓓ
4 Ⓔ Ⓕ Ⓖ Ⓗ
5 Ⓐ Ⓑ Ⓒ Ⓓ
6 Ⓔ Ⓕ Ⓖ Ⓗ

Go on to the next page.

Directions Read each sentence. Find the **adjective** in it. Then fill in the circle that has the same letter as your answer.	**Sample** The grumpy baby cried. A B C D	**Answer Column** S Ⓐ ⬤Ⓑ Ⓒ Ⓓ

		Answer Column
1 Roses often are red. A B C D	**4** Bright sunshine lit the room. E F G H	**1** Ⓐ Ⓑ Ⓒ Ⓓ **2** Ⓔ Ⓕ Ⓖ Ⓗ
2 Hungry seals bark loudly. E F G H	**5** Ellen likes fresh bread. A B C D	**3** Ⓐ Ⓑ Ⓒ Ⓓ **4** Ⓔ Ⓕ Ⓖ Ⓗ
3 Lions have long tails. A B C D	**6** Children can be noisy. E F G H	**5** Ⓐ Ⓑ Ⓒ Ⓓ **6** Ⓔ Ⓕ Ⓖ Ⓗ

Directions Read each sentence. Find the **adverb** in it. Then fill in the circle that has the same letter as your answer.	**Sample** The stars twinkle brightly. A B C D	**Answer Column** S Ⓐ Ⓑ Ⓒ ⬤Ⓓ

		Answer Column
1 Mrs. Simms sang loudly. A B C D	**4** The bus stops here. E F G H	**1** Ⓐ Ⓑ Ⓒ Ⓓ **2** Ⓔ Ⓕ Ⓖ Ⓗ
2 Young children play outside. E F G H	**5** I never eat carrots. A B C D	**3** Ⓐ Ⓑ Ⓒ Ⓓ **4** Ⓔ Ⓕ Ⓖ Ⓗ
3 Now the show will start. A B C D	**6** Our puppy ran away. E F G H	**5** Ⓐ Ⓑ Ⓒ Ⓓ **6** Ⓔ Ⓕ Ⓖ Ⓗ

Directions Read each sentence. Find the **pronoun** in it. Then fill in the circle that has the same letter as your answer.	**Sample** Roger rode his bike. A B C D	**Answer Column** S Ⓐ Ⓑ ⬤Ⓒ Ⓓ

		Answer Column
1 It is cold today. A B C D	**4** My television is broken. E F G H	**1** Ⓐ Ⓑ Ⓒ Ⓓ **2** Ⓔ Ⓕ Ⓖ Ⓗ
2 We heard a noise. E F G H	**5** Sally lost her ring. A B C D	**3** Ⓐ Ⓑ Ⓒ Ⓓ **4** Ⓔ Ⓕ Ⓖ Ⓗ
3 Patty saw me, too. A B C D	**6** An officer helped us. E F G H	**5** Ⓐ Ⓑ Ⓒ Ⓓ **6** Ⓔ Ⓕ Ⓖ Ⓗ

STOP

PUTTING IT TOGETHER

Now you know about the different kinds of words in our language. When you speak or write, you use these words together in a **certain order** to **form sentences.** You make **different kinds** of sentences for **different purposes.**

Think About   Read the sentence below. Does it make sense to you?

A fish and Elizabeth John cooked.

_____

Put the same words together in a different order. Write a sentence that makes sense.

_____

Suppose people put words together in any order they felt like. What would happen then?

_____

_____

_____

Which way of putting words together makes it easier to communicate?

_____

_____

Why?

_____

_____

_____

There are rules about how to form sentences. If we all follow the same rules, we can understand one another better.

Remember A **declarative** sentence **tells** about something. It ends with a **period (.)**. An **interrogative** sentence **asks** about something. It ends with a **question mark (?)**.

Examples Soap and paint are made from corn.
Is there corn in dog food, too?

Think About Read the examples again. Which one is a statement? Write the word DECLARATIVE after it. Which one is a question? Write the word INTERROGATIVE after it.

Apply Read the sentences. Write **D** above each declarative sentence. Write **I** above each interrogative sentence.

Have you ever been lost in the woods? Were you scared? Do you

know what to do if it happens again? Will people be looking for you?

You will be safe if you keep your head. It is best to stay in one place.

You should sit down in the middle of a trail if you can. That way,

someone will find you soon.

Apply Do some writing of your own. Tell about a time you got lost. Use declarative sentences and interrogative sentences.

_____

_____

_____

_____

_____

_____

Remember   The **word order** is different in declarative and interrogative sentences.

Examples   DECLARATIVE ▶   The play will end by noon.
INTERROGATIVE ▶   Will the play end by noon?

Think About   Read the examples again. Where is the subject in the declarative sentence? Where is the subject in the interrogative sentence?

_____

Apply   Change the word order to make these sentences interrogative.

1. You have heard a fly buzzing.

_____

2. Its wings are beating very fast.

_____

3. Some flies can move faster than birds.

_____

Remember   The question words **who, what, when,** and **where** can be used to make interrogative sentences.

Example   DECLARATIVE ▶   Georgia O'Keeffe painted desert scenes.
INTERROGATIVE ▶   What did Georgia O'Keeffe paint?

Think About   Read the examples again. What new words are added in the interrogative sentence? What word is changed?

_____

Apply   Use question words to make these sentences interrogative.

1. Garrett Morgan invented gas masks.

_____

2. He made the first one in 1912.

_____

3. In Cleveland, it saved the lives of 20 workers.

_____

Remember   An **exclamatory** sentence **shows surprise** or **strong feeling.** It ends with an **exclamation point (!).**

Examples   What an exciting dream Paul had!
How sorry he was to wake up!

Think About   Read the examples again. How does an exclamatory sentence begin?

_____

Apply   Read the sentences. Underline each exclamatory sentence.

What a terrible hurricane this is! The wind is blowing at 75 miles an hour. How loud it roars! Did you see that tree go down? What enormous waves are breaking on the beach! How scary it would be to be out in a boat!

Remember   An **imperative** sentence **asks or tells someone to do something.** It usually ends with a **period (.).** If it shows surprise or strong feeling, it ends with an **exclamation point (!).**

Examples   Rake the leaves into a pile.
Don't let them blow away!

Think About   Read the examples again. Do these sentences have a subject? If so, what is it?

_____

_____

Apply   Read the sentences. Underline each imperative sentence.

This is the way to make your garden grow. Pull up all the weeds. Get rid of all the slugs. Does the soil look a little dry? Remember to keep it damp. Be careful with the baby plants!

Apply Read these sentences. Above each one, write an abbreviation to tell what kind it is. Use **decl.** for declarative, **inter.** for interrogative, **imp.** for imperative, and **excl.** for exclamatory.

What interesting creatures spiders are! Don't ever kill one! Did you know spiders are helpful to people? They eat harmful insects.

Are spiders themselves insects? How often that question is asked! The answer is easy to discover. Just take a close look at a spider. How many legs do you see? Count them. You'll find eight legs on a spider. Insects have only six.

So what animal family do spiders belong to? They are close cousins of the lobster. What an odd fact that is!

Apply Do some writing of your own. Tell what you know about spiders. Try to use all the different kinds of sentences.

_____

_____

_____

_____

_____

Remember A sentence tells **one complete thought.** Two or more thoughts written together are not a sentence. They are a **run-on.**

Examples   RUN-ON ► Were wild boars once common in Europe they didn't look much like today's pigs.

SENTENCES ► Were wild boars once common in Europe? They didn't look much like today's pigs.

Think About Read the examples again. How do you show that a sentence is beginning? How do you show that a sentence is ending?

_____

_____

Apply Read these run-ons. Write each one correctly. Use a capital letter to begin each sentence and a punctuation mark to end it.

1. How did California get so many wild boars imagine a ship loaded with pigs sinking near Sonoma long ago.

_____

_____

_____

2. Those pigs soon became wild they had to in order to survive.

_____

_____

3. How large the herds became now people hunt the boars every year.

_____

_____

Apply Do some writing of your own. Tell how you think wild horses got to the Old West. Be sure to use complete sentences.

_____

_____

_____

_____

_____

31

- ✔ You use a **declarative** sentence to **tell** something. You end it with a **period.**

- ✔ You use an **interrogative** sentence to **ask** something. You end it with a **question mark.**

- ✔ You use an **exclamatory** sentence to **show surprise** or **strong feeling.** You end it with an **exclamation point.**

- ✔ You use an **imperative** sentence to **ask or tell someone to do something.** You end it with a **period** or an **exclamation point.**

- ✔ You use a **capital letter** to begin each sentence. You use this signal and end punctuation to separate **run-ons.**

When you proofread, you use special marks.

≡ means "Make this a capital letter."   ⊙ means "Add a period."

∧ means "Add here."

Use these proofreading marks to correct the travel guide's speech below. Separate the run-ons with capital letters and end punctuation.

how many of you know what a volcano is it's really just an opening in the earth's surface. When it erupts, hot gases and melted rock burst out. can you imagine a temperature of 2,000° F? How hot that rock is what a wide path it burns down the mountain!

The name of this volcano is Kilauea do you want to see the place where it erupted last week? Please watch your step stay on the path. Keep away from the hot ash how powerful Kilauea is!

Remember A sentence has different parts. The **simple subject** is the **noun** or **pronoun** that the sentence tells about. The **complete subject** is that **main word and all of the words that tell about it.**

Example   COMPLETE SUBJECT
                     ▼
Several different <u>plants</u> grow in deep water.
                     ▲
            SIMPLE SUBJECT

Think About Read the example again. What is the difference between the simple subject and the complete subject?

_____

_____

Apply Read the sentences. Underline the complete subject in each one. Circle the simple subject.

Many ponds are covered with water lilies. Their long, tough stalks grow up from the mud. Their round, flat leaves lie on the surface of the water. Many different insects sit on the leaves. The large, white blossoms can be one foot across.

These remarkable flowers are useful as well as beautiful. Their roots suck plant and animal wastes out of the water. A few plants can really clean up a dirty pond.

Apply Do some writing of your own. Tell about an interesting plant that you see every day. Then underline each complete subject in your sentences. Circle each simple subject.

_____

_____

_____

_____

Remember The **simple predicate** is the **verb** or **verb phrase** that tells what the subject does or is. The **complete predicate** is that **main word and all of the words that tell about it.**

Examples

COMPLETE PREDICATE
▼
Scientists <u>send spaceships to the moon.</u>
The spaceships <u>will bring moon rocks back to earth.</u>
▲
SIMPLE PREDICATE

Think About Read the examples again. Is the simple predicate always just one word?

_____

Apply Read the sentences. Underline the complete predicate in each one. Circle the simple predicate.

The Ebony Museum is in Oakland, California. It shows only African and African-American art. The owner of the Ebony Museum is named Aissatoui Vernita. Vernita has been collecting art since 1968. She has bought the work of many black American artists. She collects African sculptures, too. The museum is a very special place. Its many visitors agree.

Apply Do some writing of your own. Tell about something that you like to collect. Then underline each complete predicate in your sentences. Circle each simple predicate.

_____

_____

_____

_____

34

Remember   Sometimes two short sentences have the same predicate. Then the subjects can be joined by the word **and** to make a **compound subject.**

Example   ▼ SUBJECT

<u>Tortillas</u> are made with corn flour.
<u>Tamales</u> are made with corn flour.

▼ COMPOUND SUBJECT

<u>Tortillas and tamales</u> are made with corn flour.

Think About   Read the example again. How is a compound subject different from a simple subject?

_____

Apply   Read each pair of sentences. Write them as one sentence with a compound subject joined by the word **and.**

1. Papayas are eaten for dessert in Mexico. Guavas are eaten for dessert in Mexico.

_____

_____

2. Spices add flavor to Mexican chocolate. Almonds add flavor to Mexican chocolate.

_____

_____

3. Pilar loves Mexican food. I love Mexican food.

_____

_____

Apply   Do some writing of your own. Tell about two of your favorite foods. Use a compound subject.

_____

_____

_____

_____

Remember Sometimes two short sentences have the same subject. Then the predicates can be joined by the word **and** to make a **compound predicate.**

Example   PREDICATE ▼

A sailboat <u>tipped over</u>.

A sailboat <u>sank</u>.

COMPOUND PREDICATE ▼

A sailboat <u>tipped over and sank</u>.

Think About Read the example again. How is a compound predicate different from a simple predicate?

_____

Apply Read each pair of sentences. Write them as one sentence with a compound predicate joined by the word **and.**

1. The people in the sailboat climbed onto their raft. The people in the sailboat waited.

_____

_____

2. They shouted at passing boats. They waved at passing boats.

_____

_____

3. Finally someone saw them. Finally someone stopped to help.

_____

_____

Apply Do some writing of your own. Tell about two things that you will do to help someone today. Use a compound predicate.

_____

_____

_____

_____

Remember Sometimes two short sentences can be joined by the word **and, but,** or **or** to make a **compound sentence. And** joins sentences that tell about **similar** things. **But** joins sentences that tell about things that are **different. Or** joins sentences that give a **choice** between things.

Examples Whales sometimes swim ashore, <u>and</u> no one knows why.
These mammals breathe air, <u>but</u> they cannot live on land.
They must be pulled out to sea, <u>or</u> they will die.

Think About Read the examples again. How many thoughts are there in a compound sentence?

_____

Apply Read each pair of sentences. A compound sentence has been started to join them. Write **and, but,** or **or.** Then write the second half of the sentence.

1. Jamestown was founded by English settlers. Plymouth was founded by English settlers, too.

Jamestown was founded by English settlers, _____

_____

2. The settlers could fight with the Native Americans. They could make friends with them.

The settlers could fight with the Native Americans, _____

_____

3. Only men lived in Jamestown at first. Families lived in Plymouth.

Only men lived in Jamestown at first, _____

_____

 Apply Do some writing of your own. Tell two things that you know about early settlers in America.

_____

_____

_____

_____

- ✔ You tell what a sentence is about in the **complete subject.** You use a noun or pronoun as the **simple subject.**
- ✔ You tell what the subject does or is in the **complete predicate.** You use a verb or verb phrase as the **simple predicate.**
- ✔ You use the word **and** to make **compound subjects** and **compound predicates.**
- ✔ You use the words **and, but,** and **or** to make **compound sentences.**

Read this report. Write **compound subject** above each sentence with a compound subject. Write **compound predicate** above each sentence with a compound predicate. Write **compound sentence** above each compound sentence.

Everyone has read "Cinderella," and everyone remembers

Cinderella's glass slipper. Was it really glass? You and I always

thought so. Your parents probably thought so and told you so. Many

books call it a glass slipper, too, but the books are wrong.

Cinderella's slipper was made of fur. "Cinderella" is a French story,

and the French word for *glass* sounds like the word for *fur.* So

people heard wrong and got the story mixed up. A fur slipper and

a glass slipper are quite different. Do you like the story better as it

is now, or do you prefer the older story?

Remember   A **paragraph** is a group of sentences that tells about **one main idea.** The main idea is stated in a **topic sentence.**

Example   ▼ TOPIC SENTENCE

Kangaroos are strange-looking animals. They have very short front legs and very large back legs. They sit up like rabbits, but they are seven feet high. Besides that, some kangaroos are bright red.

Think About   Read the example again. How is the first line written?

_____

Apply   Read each paragraph. Underline the topic sentence.

Kangaroos are good jumpers. In just one jump, they can cover 25 feet. They leap up to 40 miles an hour.

Mother kangaroos carry their babies in a pouch. The pouch is on the mother kangaroo's stomach. The baby crawls into it as soon as it is born. It stays there for about six months. Even after the baby learns to walk, it still rides in its mother's pouch sometimes.

People are kangaroos' main enemy. Hunters kill them for their meat and fur. Farmers kill them because they eat the farm animals' grass.

Apply   Write a paragraph of your own. Tell about another strange-looking animal. Underline the topic sentence of your paragraph.

_____

_____

_____

_____

_____

39

Remember   The **topic sentence** states the **main idea** of a paragraph. All of the other sentences give **details** about the main idea. If a sentence doesn't tell about the main idea, it doesn't belong in the paragraph. A **new paragraph** is begun for **each new main idea.**

Example   Farmers raise dairy cattle for their milk. A good dairy cow will provide 1,600 gallons of milk a year.

Ranchers raise beef cattle for their meat. They can get about 400 pounds of meat from an 800-pound steer.

Think About   Read the example again. Why are there two paragraphs?

_____

_____

Apply   Read the sentences. They tell about two main ideas. Write them as two paragraphs. Indent the first line of each one. Leave out the sentences that do not belong.

Beef cattle need plenty of good food. In summer they eat grass. In winter they get hay. It snowed last winter. There is beef in many of the things we eat. Hot dogs have beef in them. I like mustard on my hot dogs. Some kinds of chili are made with beef. And did you know that there is beef in mince pie?

_____

_____

_____

_____

_____

_____

_____

40

Remember   The sentences of a paragraph have to be in the **right order.** They often follow the **time order** of events.

Example   In the 1800s many Western towns were busy places. Later, there were no jobs, so all the people left. Today, these towns are just empty buildings. We call them ghost towns.

Think About   Read the example again. What three times does the paragraph tell about?

_____

Apply   Read the sentences. Decide on the time order of the events. Then write the sentences in the correct order to make a paragraph.

For a while after that, Dodge City was almost a ghost town. In the 1870s cowboys brought huge herds of cattle through Dodge City, Kansas. Today it is a busy city again. It was a busy city. Then in the 1890s the cowboys stopped coming because trains began taking cattle to market.

_____
_____
_____
_____
_____
_____
_____

Apply   Write a paragraph of your own. Tell something about the history of your state, your town, or your school. Be sure to write your sentences in the correct time order. Underline your topic sentence.

_____
_____
_____
_____
_____

REVIEW TIME

- When you write, you **organize** your sentences into **paragraphs.** In each paragraph you tell about **one main idea.**

- You **begin a new paragraph** for each main idea by **indenting** the first line.

- You often state your main idea in a **topic sentence.** You use other sentences in the paragraph to give **details** about the main idea.

- You arrange the sentences of a paragraph in the **right order.** Often you follow the time order of events.

When you proofread, you use special marks.

~~WORDS~~ means "Take out."   ⸆ means "Start a new paragraph."

Use these proofreading marks to correct the report below. Take out sentences that don't belong and start a new paragraph for each main idea.

Millions of people are moving from the country to the city. There are over 5 billion people in the world. In 1985, only 11 cities in the world had more than 10 million people. By the year 2000, there will be 22 cities that big.

Why are so many people moving to the city? It's easier for them to find jobs there. Work hard if you want to succeed. And cities can be more fun to live in because they have more things to do. But sometimes people are worse off in the city. Things are more expensive. Money doesn't grow on trees. There is usually more crime, too.

WRITING TIME

An **adventure story** tells about an exciting time that somebody had. You try to make the reader feel what it was like.

Write an adventure story with yourself as the hero or heroine. Tell about something exciting that really happened to you. Or tell about an imaginary adventure. Make some notes to help you.

When and where does your adventure happen? _____

_____

What problems do you have? Do you have to escape from something? Find something?

Do something? Get somewhere? _____

_____

How do you try to solve the problem? _____

_____

How does the adventure end? Do you solve the problem or not? _____

_____

Now write your adventure story. Follow these steps.

1. Use scratch paper for your first copy. Write the whole story.

2. Show your writing to a friend. Talk about how to make it more exciting.

3. Revise your story. Take out things you don't like and add new things. Be sure to use a variety of sentences. Organize your sentences in the right time order. Combine sentences if you can.

4. Now proofread your work. Check your spelling and end punctuation. Be sure to indent paragraphs.

5. When your story is ready, copy it neatly onto a clean sheet of paper.

6. Share your story with the class.

Look at this picture of the baseball game. Write a story about this picture. Use a separate sheet of paper.

TEST TIME

Directions Read each sentence. Decide **what kind** of sentence it is. Fill in the circle that has the same letter as your answer.

Sample

Where is my pen

A declarative

B interrogative

C imperative

D exclamatory

Answer Column

S Ⓐ ⬤Ⓑ Ⓒ Ⓓ

---

1 Please don't open the window

A declarative

B interrogative

C imperative

D exclamatory

2 Ollie broke his glasses

E declarative

F interrogative

G imperative

H exclamatory

3 Have you eaten yet

A declarative

B interrogative

C imperative

D exclamatory

4 What a heavy rock this is

E declarative

F interrogative

G imperative

H exclamatory

5 I like going to movies

A declarative

B interrogative

C imperative

D exclamatory

6 How hot that fire is

E declarative

F interrogative

G imperative

H exclamatory

7 Move your feet

A declarative

B interrogative

C imperative

D exclamatory

8 When is Kate's party

E declarative

F interrogative

G imperative

H exclamatory

1 Ⓐ Ⓑ Ⓒ Ⓓ
2 Ⓔ Ⓕ Ⓖ Ⓗ
3 Ⓐ Ⓑ Ⓒ Ⓓ
4 Ⓔ Ⓕ Ⓖ Ⓗ
5 Ⓐ Ⓑ Ⓒ Ⓓ
6 Ⓔ Ⓕ Ⓖ Ⓗ
7 Ⓐ Ⓑ Ⓒ Ⓓ
8 Ⓔ Ⓕ Ⓖ Ⓗ

Go on to the next page.

45

Directions Read the paragraph. Then read the questions about it. Fill in the circle below the correct answer.

Sample (1)   Horse trainers have a hard job.
(2) King Glorious is a remarkable racehorse.
(3) He won a $1 million prize in Hollywood in 1988.
(4) He also came in second in the Kentucky Derby.

Which sentence is the topic sentence?

Which sentence does not belong?

      1 2 3 4
     ○ ● ○ ○
     ● ○ ○ ○

---

1 (1)   Sometimes people get sunburned.
(2) Your skin protects you.
(3) It also controls your body heat.
(4) Your skin does many important jobs.

Which sentence is the topic sentence?

Which sentence does not belong?

      1 2 3 4
     ○ ○ ○ ○
     ○ ○ ○ ○

---

2 (1)   Your brain tells your body what to do.
(2) It tells you how to walk, run, and jump.
(3) It even tells your heart how to beat.
(4) Some people have large heads.

Which sentence is the topic sentence?

Which sentence does not belong?

      1 2 3 4
     ○ ○ ○ ○
     ○ ○ ○ ○

---

3 (1)   Not all bones are the same.
(2) How many bones are in your hand?
(3) Some bones are long.
(4) Other bones are short.

Which sentence is the topic sentence?

Which sentence does not belong?

      1 2 3 4
     ○ ○ ○ ○
     ○ ○ ○ ○

CHANGING WORDS

When you put words together in sentences, you sometimes have to **change** them. The different kinds of words change in different ways.

Think About   Look at these nouns.

hat   hats   hat's

How is the second noun different from the first one?

_____

When the spelling changed, how did the meaning change?

_____

How is the third noun different from the first one?

_____

When the spelling changed, how did the meaning change?

_____

Now think of a verb that names an action that you might want to tell about. How many ways do you know to write this verb? List them.

_____

_____

Did the meaning of the verb change every time you changed the spelling?

_____

Words sometimes have to be changed, depending on how you use them. You might have to add letters to a word or spell it differently. You want your reader to understand what you write, and you won't be there to explain.

Remember   A **suffix** is a **letter** or **a group of letters** that is added to the **end** of a word to **change the meaning.** The **plural form** of most nouns is made by adding a suffix.

Examples   SINGULAR ▶   day + s = day<u>s</u>   ◀ PLURAL
                                pass + es = pass<u>es</u>
                                ax + es = ax<u>es</u>
                                wish + es = wish<u>es</u>
                                catch + es = catch<u>es</u>

Think About   Read the examples again. What two suffixes are added to make plural nouns? For what kinds of nouns is each suffix used?

_____

_____

Apply   Read the sentences. Write the plural form of the noun that is under each line.

_____ are little _____ with brightly colored
         Sphinx   moth

_____ . You can find them resting on tall _____ in
   wing   grass

_____ of bright sunlight. Look for them in _____ ,
   patch   bush

too. These _____ feed on _____ , just as
              insect   flower

_____ do. Try collecting some. You can fit
   hummingbird

_____ of the beautiful moths in glass _____ .
   bunch   box

Apply   Do some writing of your own. Tell about other insects that you would like to study or collect.

_____

_____

_____

_____

Remember   Sometimes a **change** must be made in the **root word** when a suffix is added.

Examples   SINGULAR ▶   hobby → hobb**i** + es = hobb**ies** ◀ PLURAL

party → part**i** + es = part**ies**

Think About   Read the examples again. How do the root words change?

_____

Apply   Read the sentences. Write plural forms to complete them.

Both of Grandma Daisy's _____ fought in the Civil
                                  granddaddy

War. The Union and Confederate _____ were fighting over slavery.
                                       army

Many free black men from northern _____ joined the Union army.
                                           city

Grandma tells _____ about her granddaddy Ab. He was one of
                        story

the best _____ the Union had.
              spy

Remember   Some **plural forms** are made by **changing the spelling.**

Examples   SINGULAR ▶   mouse → m**ice** ◀ PLURAL

tooth → t**eeth**

Think About   Read the examples again. Are these two plural forms made

the same way? _____

Apply   Read the sentences. Write plural forms to complete them. Use a dictionary if you need help.

Grandma Daisy's granddaddy Jim was one of the black _____
                                                              man

in the Union army. He took care of the mules and _____ that pulled
                                                        ox

the supply wagons. He marched all day; he said the war was hard on his

_____ . Ab and Jim were brave, good _____ .
   foot   person

49

- ✔ You add **suffixes** to words to **change their meanings.**
- ✔ You can use suffixes to make nouns **plural.** For most nouns, you add **s** or **es.** For some nouns, you **change the root word** before adding the plural ending. For other nouns, you completely **change the spelling** to make the plural form.

When you proofread, you use special marks.

~~WORD~~ means "Take out."   ∧ means "Add here."

Use these proofreading marks to correct the report below.

Have you ever seen a border collie herding sheep? These doges are

used on many Western ranchs. They take their dutys very seriously

indeed. They have sharp tooths and make lightning passies at the sheep.

They nip at the animals' foots to make them move.

The border collie is one of the smartest animals around. That's what

peoples who work with them say. Their good memorys make them easy

to train. They love to obey their masteres and mistresss. The mother dog

often trains her puppys herself. Mans and womans who raise sheep think

of their border collies as their partneres.

Remember The **tense** of a verb tells **when** the action happens. A verb in the **future tense** tells about something that is going to happen.

Example MAIN VERB ▶ take

FUTURE ▶ Tomorrow, we <u>will take</u> a plane to West Berlin.

Think About Read the example again. What helping verb is used to make the future tense? _____

Apply Read the sentences. Rewrite each one with the helping verb **will** to make it tell about the future.

1. People in many communist countries have freedom at last.

_____

_____

2. East and West Germany become one country.

_____

_____

3. East Germans visit their relatives in West Germany.

_____

_____

4. Some of them see their mothers for the first time in 40 years.

_____

_____

5. People take home pieces of the Berlin Wall for their friends.

_____

_____

 Apply Do some writing of your own. Tell about something you hope will happen soon.

_____

_____

_____

_____

Remember A verb in the **present tense** tells about what is happening **now** or **all the time.** Its form changes to agree with the sentence subject. **Just the verb** is used with a **plural subject** and with the pronouns **you** and **I.** With a **singular subject,** a **suffix** is added to the verb.

Examples PLURAL, *YOU, I* ► The teams <u>play</u> each Saturday.
I <u>pitch</u> sometimes.

SINGULAR ► Our team <u>plays</u> well.
Jodi <u>pitches</u> even better than I do.

Think About What two suffixes are added to make verbs agree with

singular subjects? _____ For what kinds of verbs is each suffix used?

_____

Apply Read the sentences. Write the correct form of the verb that is under each line.

Some words _____ just like the noises they _____.
        sound   describe

A bee _____ and _____ while a snake _____ . A hungry
        hum   buzz   hiss

boy _____ an apple and then _____ his lips. A rusty gate
        bite   smack

_____ until someone _____ it with oil. And ice cubes
  screech   fix

_____ into a glass, making sodas _____ .
  plop   fizz

Apply Do some writing of your own. Use some sound words, like *crash* and *swish*, that you like.

_____

_____

_____

_____

Remember   Sometimes a **change** must be made in the **root word** when a suffix is added.

Example   PLURAL, *YOU, I* ► Airplanes <u>fly</u> forward.
              SINGULAR ► A helicopter <u>flies</u> up and down as well.

Think About   Read the example again. How does the root word change?

_____

Apply   Read the sentences. Write the correct form of the verb that is under each line.

A squirrel _____ an acorn in its mouth. The animal
                  carry

_____ the acorn in the ground. Then it _____ off
   bury   hurry

to find another. I _____ about one thing: All the squirrels
                        worry

_____ to find their buried food at the same time. How
   try

do you suppose each squirrel _____ its own?
                                   identify

Remember   For some verbs the **spelling is changed** to make the verb agree with the subject.

Examples   PLURAL, *YOU, I* ► Most fish <u>have</u> scales.
               SINGULAR ► An angelfish <u>has</u> stripes.

Think About   Read the examples again. Which spelling is used with a plural subject, **you,** or **I?** _____ Which is used with a singular subject? _____

Apply   Read the sentences. Write **have** or **has** to complete each one.

You _____ lots of tropical fish. The two pearl gouramis _____

white spots and long whiskers. The only catfish _____ whiskers, too,

but they are short. Make sure your pets _____ green plants to hide in.

And be sure the aquarium always _____ clean water, too.

53

REVIEW TIME

- ✔ You make the **future tense** of verbs by adding the helping verb **will.**
- ✔ You use two forms of **present-tense** verbs. With **plural subjects** and the pronouns **you** and **I,** you use **just the verb.** With **singular subjects,** you add the suffix **s** or **es** to the verb. For some verbs, you **change the root word** before you add the suffix.
- ✔ You use **have** with **plural subjects** and with the pronouns **you** and **I.** You use **has** with **singular subjects.**

When you proofread, you use special marks.

~~WORDS~~ means "Take out."   ∧   means "Add here."

Use these proofreading marks to correct the article below.

People sees killer bees in California fairly often. These bees comes up

from South America. Each year, the insect fly a little farther north. The

killer bee has a strong poison in its stinger. These bees also has mean

tempers. They attacks any animal that disturbs their nest. The killer bee

also push other bees out of the area. It wish to have the whole world for

itself.

The honeybee supply us with honey. It carry pollen from one plant to

another. If the killer bee chase it away, crops not grow anymore. Then

everyone suffer.

54

Remember A verb in the **past tense** tells about what has **already** happened. The past tense of most verbs is made by adding a suffix.

Examples VERB ▶ polish + ed = polish<u>ed</u> ◀ PAST TENSE
rule + ed = rul<u>ed</u>

Think About Read the examples again. What suffix is added to make the past tense of most verbs? _____ What happens to the root word of verbs that end in **e?** _____

Apply Read the sentences. Write the past form of the verb that is under each line.

Long ago, Japanese soldiers _____ in
dress

beautiful armor. The iron cloth _____
protect

them very well. The Japanese soldier especially

_____ his helmet. It often _____
prize   save

his life. An iron collar _____ his neck
cover

between the helmet and the armor. The soldier

also _____ an iron mask. The fierce face
use

_____ enemies. Two swords
frighten

_____ the soldier's equipment.
complete

Apply Do some writing of your own. Describe a uniform or costume that you have worn in the past.

_____

_____

_____

_____

Remember Sometimes a **change** must be made in the **root word** when a suffix is added.

Examples VERB ► fry → fr<u>i</u> + ed = fr<u>ied</u> ◄ PAST TENSE
copy → cop<u>i</u> + ed = cop<u>ied</u>

Think About Read the examples again. If a verb ends in a **consonant plus y,** how is the root word changed when **ed** is added?

_____

Apply Read the sentences. Write the past tense of the verb that is under each line.

Jacques Cousteau _____ sea animals. He _____
study   worry

about our oceans. For years, rivers _____ pollution into
carry

the sea. Cousteau _____ to warn people about this. He
try

_____ for laws to keep the oceans clean.
lobby

Remember Sometimes a **change** must be made in the **root word** when a suffix is added.

Examples VERB ► beg → beg<u>g</u> + ed = beg<u>ged</u> ◄ PAST TENSE
dim → dim<u>m</u> + ed = dim<u>med</u>

Think About Read the examples again. Both verbs are one syllable and end in a consonant-vowel-consonant. What change must be made in the root word when the past-tense suffix **ed** is added?

_____

Apply Read the sentences. Write the past tense of the verb that is under each line.

The police officer _____ her fingers. Her trained dog
snap

_____ the package and _____ it open. At another command,
grab   rip

the dog _____. The partners had _____ another crook.
stop   trap

56

REVIEW TIME

- ✔ You make the **past tense** of most verbs by adding **ed.**
- ✔ For some verbs, you also **change the root word** before adding the suffix.

When you proofread, you use special marks.

~~WORDS~~ means "Take out."   ∧ means "Add here."

Use these proofreading marks to correct the travel report below. Make the report in the past tense.

For thousands of years, the people of Tahiti fish for food. Sometimes

the women wade into shallow water. Then they spear the fish swimming

there. The men usually sail out to sea every day. Each boat carry big nets.

The fishermen drop the nets into the ocean. Then they drag them slowly

through the water. They try to catch enough to feed their families. But

they also hope to get a few extra. Then they trade the fish for other

goods.

Remember The **past tense** of some verbs is made by **changing their spelling.**

Examples

	PRESENT ►	make	go	see	grow
	PAST ►	ma<u>d</u>e	<u>went</u>	s<u>aw</u>	gr<u>ew</u>
	PRESENT ►	bring	do	give	become
	PAST ►	br<u>ought</u>	d<u>id</u>	g<u>a</u>ve	bec<u>a</u>me

Think About Read the examples again. Is a suffix always added to a verb to make the past form?

_____

Apply Read the sentences. Write the past tense of the verb that is under each line. Use the examples to help you.

Alfred Nobel _____ up in Sweden. He
  grow

_____ wealthy by inventing dynamite. It
  become

_____ him millions of dollars. But Alfred
  bring

_____ that his invention could be harmful. People
  see

_____ dangerous weapons with it. So Alfred
  make

_____ something special. He_____ his money
  do   give

away when he died. Nobel Prizes _____ to people for
  go

science, literature, and peace.

Apply Now do some writing of your own. Tell about an award or prize that you once won or wanted to win.

_____

_____

_____

_____

_____

58

Remember The **past tense** of some verbs is made by **changing their spelling** or by making **no change** at all.

Examples PRESENT ▶ drive → dr<u>o</u>ve ◀ PAST
put → put

Think About Read the examples again. You already know that the past tenses of verbs are made in different ways. How can you find out how a verb changes?

_____

_____

Apply Read the sentences. Write the past tense of the verb that is under each line. Use a dictionary if you need help.

In the past, people _____ horses or walked over the Alps. Then
ride

the Swiss _____ a highway through the mountains. So many people
build

_____ through the Alps that air pollution _____ hurting the
drive   begin

forests. Many trees _____ sick and died. Experts _____ about
get   write

the problem. Soon people _____ they had to do something about it.
know

They _____ the experts' advice and _____ down on the
take   cut

pollution from cars.

Apply Do some writing of your own. Tell about something that you know once caused air pollution.

_____

_____

_____

_____

_____

Remember   **Past-tense** verbs can also be made using the helping verbs **have, has,** and **had.** For most verbs, the **usual past form** is used with the helping verb.

Examples   have <u>worked</u>   has <u>saved</u>   had <u>hurried</u>

have <u>rubbed</u>   has <u>brought</u>   had <u>cut</u>

Think About   Read the examples again. How many words are used for each past-tense verb? _____

Apply   Read the sentences. Write the correct past tense of the verb that is under each line.

By the 1890s people had _____ almost
                                      kill

all of the snowy egrets. They had _____
                                              trap

millions of these birds in enormous nets. They had

_____ their feathers to decorate ladies'
     use

hats. Bird lovers have _____ hard to protect
                              try

the snowy egret. Now they have _____ a
                                          find

way to do it. The Lacey Act has _____ it
                                        make

illegal to sell the feathers of wild birds. Now people

have _____ killing the egrets. The Lacey
        stop

Act has _____ these birds from extinction.
              save

Apply   Do some writing of your own. Tell about a fashion that you think should be against the law. Tell why you think so.

_____

_____

_____

Remember Some verbs have a **special past form** to use with **have, has,** and **had.**

Examples

PRESENT ►	go	give	do	get
PAST ►	went	gave	did	got
SPECIAL PAST ►	gone	given	done	gotten
PRESENT ►	throw	take	fall	draw
PAST ►	threw	took	fell	drew
SPECIAL PAST ►	thrown	taken	fallen	drawn

Cynthia <u>threw</u> the javelin 150 feet. She always <u>has thrown</u> well.

Think About Read the examples again. How many forms of each verb are shown? _____

Apply Read the sentences. Write the correct past form of the verb that is under each line. Use the examples above to help you.

The U.S.S.R. has _____ many Olympic gold medals in wrestling.
                    take

Japan and Korea have _____ well in wrestling, too. Recently, the
                        do

U.S. _____ two firsts in freestyle wrestling. Ken Monday _____
        get   throw

his opponent in the 163-pound class. Even before that, John Smith had

_____ the crowd a good show, and his opponent _____ hard.
    give   fall

Since 800 B.C., people have _____ to the Olympic Games to see the
                                go

wrestling. This sport always has _____ a big crowd.
                                    draw

Apply Do some writing of your own. Tell about your favorite sport.

_____

_____

_____

Remember   Some verbs have a **special past form** to use with **have, has,** and **had.**

Examples

PRESENT ►	choose	eat	begin	write
PAST ►	chose	ate	began	wrote
SPECIAL PAST ►	chosen	eaten	begun	written
PRESENT ►	fly	ride	see	know
PAST ►	flew	rode	saw	knew
SPECIAL PAST ►	flown	ridden	seen	known

Joe <u>flew</u> to New York. It was the first time he <u>had flown</u> alone.

Think About   Read the examples again. Are there any rules that can help you to learn these special past forms?

_____

Apply   Read the sentences. Write the correct past form of the verb under each line. Use the examples above to help you.

In the 1970s, explorers _____ books about the Tasaday tribe.

write

They said that this tribe never had _____ how to grow crops. They

know

never had _____ anything made of metal. They never had _____

see ride

in cars. They never had _____ in airplanes. And they never

fly

_____ Western food. Many readers _____ to believe this story.

eat choose

Then some scholars _____ to suspect that it wasn't true.

begin

Apply   Do some writing of your own. Tell about an amazing story that you have heard. Or make up your own amazing story.

_____

_____

_____

_____

REVIEW TIME

- For some verbs, you **change the spelling** to make the **past tense,** or you may make **no change** at all.
- You can also use the helping verbs **have, had,** and **had** to tell about the past. You use the **usual past form** of most verbs with these helping verbs. For some verbs, you use a **special past form.**

When you proofread, you use special marks.

~~WORDS~~ means "Take out." ∧ means "Add here."

Use these proofreading marks to correct the report below.

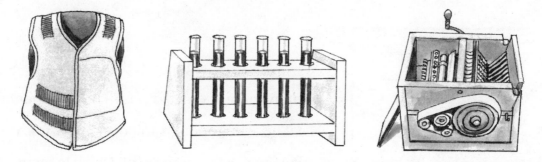

Women have invent many useful things. In 1793 Catherine Greene

helpped Eli Whitney to invent the cotton gin. It separateed the seeds from

the cotton. In 1928 Margorite Joyner taken out the first patent on a

permanent wave machine. Her invention maked her rich, and she gived

money generously to black charities. In 1965 Stephanie Kwolek finded out

how to make plastic that stoped bullets. People have use her invention to

make bulletproof vests. Women have took out even more patents in recent

years. That's because more women have studyed chemistry and the other

sciences.

Remember   The verb **be** can be a helping verb or a linking verb. It has several forms. **Am, is,** and **are** are **present** forms.

Examples   Bingo <u>is</u> a beautiful cat.
Her kittens <u>are</u> growing up fast.
You <u>are</u> getting the best one.
I <u>am</u> glad.

Think About   Read the examples again. Which present form of **be** is used with the pronoun **I?** _____ Which form is used with singular subjects? _____ Which form is used with plural subjects and the pronoun **you?** _____

Apply   Read the sentences. Write the correct present form of **be** to complete each one.

I _____ studying glaciers. A glacier _____ an enormous sheet of ice. The continental glaciers _____ big enough to cover Antarctica. A valley glacier _____ a river of ice that moves down a valley. Glaciers _____ moving all the time. Most of them _____ very, very slow. But Hubbard Glacier _____ speeding along at over five miles an hour. If you _____ going to visit Hubbard Glacier, I _____ ready to go with you!

Apply   Do some writing of your own. Tell two other things that you know about glaciers. Use an encyclopedia if you need help.

_____

_____

_____

_____

_____

Remember The **past** forms of the verb **be** are **was, were,** and **been.**

Examples America <u>was</u> part of Great Britain until 1776.
Most towns <u>were</u> very small in those days.
But Williamsburg, Virginia, <u>had been</u> important since the 1600s.

Think About Read the examples again. Which past form of **be** is used with singular subjects? _____ Which form is used with plural subjects and the pronoun **you?** _____ Which form is used with the helping verbs **have, has,** and **had?** _____

Apply Read the sentences. Write the correct past form of **be** to complete each one.

In the 1700s, Williamsburg _____ a rich, busy town. Since 1699, it had _____ the capital of Virginia. All sorts of important things _____ happening there. Then the capital _____ moved, and Williamsburg grew quiet. Since 1926, though, people have _____ working to save the old parts of town. The old houses _____ fixed up. Soon guides _____ showing visitors around. Did you see them in their colonial costumes? You _____ lucky.

Apply Do some writing of your own. Tell about something that happened when your town or state was just starting.

_____

_____

_____

_____

_____

65

Remember When the verb **be** is used as a helping verb, the suffix **ing** is often added to the **main verb.** For some verbs the **root word** is also **changed.**

Examples   VERB ►   fly   race
             WITH *BE* ►   The bird is <u>flying</u>.   The boys were <u>racing</u>.

Think About   Read the examples again. What change is made in the root word if the verb ends in **e?**

_____

Apply   Read the sentences. Write a form of **be** and add the suffix **ing** to the main verb under the line to complete each one.

For years, ranchers _____ sagebrush.
                                          kill

Today, scientists _____ this desert plant. They
                                    study

_____ to show ranchers why it should not be killed. In
          hope

the past, the ranchers _____ the sagebrush
                                          burn

because their herds _____ to eat it. But wild animals
                                    refuse

_____ in the sagebrush. Without it, those animals
              live

_____ . It is better not to kill plants that
            disappear

wild animals _____ . Where else can they go?
                          use

Apply   Do some writing of your own. Tell about another desert plant you know about.

_____

_____

_____

_____

_____

66

Remember Sometimes a **change** must be made in the **root word** when a suffix is added.

Examples VERB ► skip → skip**p** + ing = skipp**ing** ◄ WITH *BE*
jog → jog**g** + ing = jogg**ing**

Think About Read the examples again. Both verbs are one syllable and end in a consonant-vowel-consonant. What change must be made in the root word when the suffix **ing** is added?

_____

Apply Read the sentences. Write a form of **be** and add the suffix **ing** to the main verb under the line to complete each one.

For 70 years, the government of the U.S.S.R.

_____ free speech. The old
ban

rulers _____ people in prison
put

if they spoke out. Now Mikhail Gorbachev _____ up a
set

new government. He has freed the people who _____
rot

in prison. He _____ the old rulers of their power.
strip

His enemies _____ against him. But nothing
plot

_____ Gorbachev. Many people are happy that he
stop

_____ .
win

Apply Do some writing of your own. Tell two things about the government of the U.S.S.R. Look in a newspaper or an encyclopedia if you need help.

_____

_____

_____

_____

✔ You use the verb **be** as a **helping verb** or as a **linking verb.** It has several forms.

✔ In the **present tense,** you use **am** with the subject **I.** You use **is** with **singular** subjects. You use **are** with **plural** subjects and with the pronoun **you.**

✔ In the **past tense,** you use **was** with **singular** subjects. You use **were** with **plural** subjects and with the pronoun **you.** You use **been** with the helping verbs **have, has,** and **had.**

✔ When you use **be** as a helping verb, you often add **ing** to the main verb. For some verbs, you also have to **change the root word.**

When you proofread, you use special marks.

~~WORD~~ means "Take out." ⌃ means "Add here."

Use these proofreading marks to correct the article below.

Roberta Flack has being famous for a long time.

Years ago, she were workking as a schoolteacher.

However, she be very musical. Both her mother

and her father had be singers. Roberta were

hopeing to have a career in music, too. Soon she singing at a club every

evening. One night she been lucky. She was heard by some people who

was work for a record company. The next thing she knew, they was

inviteing her to make a record. It am a big success, and she went on to

make more records. Today Roberta Flack are a popular singer and

songwriter. Is you a fan of hers?

Remember An **adjective** can be used to **compare nouns.** For most short adjectives, **suffixes** are used to make the comparing forms.

Examples   ADJECTIVE ►   small + er = small<u>er</u>   ◄ COMPARING TWO
small + est = small<u>est</u>   ◄ COMPARING MORE

Think About Read the examples again. What suffix is added to compare two nouns? _____ What suffix is used to compare three or more? _____

Apply Read the sentences. Write the correct comparing form of the adjective that is under each line.

The _____ kind of kite is the flat kite. It is _____
old   old

than almost any other toy. Box kites are _____ to fly than other
hard

kites. To keep them up, you have to be much _____ than your
smart

friends. The _____ kites in the world are made in Japan.
tall

They are even _____ than the people who fly them. In Asia, the
tall

_____ kites are used for kite fights. And the _____
fast   odd

kites moan and whistle as they fly.

Apply Do some writing of your own. Tell about the best game you ever played. Tell why it was better than any other game.

_____

_____

_____

_____

Remember   Sometimes the **root word** must be **changed** before a suffix is added to an adjective.

Examples   ADJECTIVE ▼   ▼ COMPARING TWO

           happy → happ<u>i</u> + er = happ<u>ier</u>

           happy → happ<u>i</u> + est = happ<u>iest</u>

                                     ▲ COMPARING MORE

Think About   Read the examples again. How does an adjective that ends in **a consonant plus y** change when the comparing forms are made?

_____

Apply   Read the sentences. Write comparing forms to complete them.

The _____ weather is near the ocean. It is often much
        foggy

_____ in the mountains. Clouds are the _____
   windy   heavy

everywhere just before a storm, and winter is usually _____
                                          stormy

than fall. The South is the _____ place to be then.
                         sunny

Remember   Different adjectives change in different ways when the comparing suffixes are added.

Examples   ADJECTIVE ►   pale →   pal + er = pal<u>er</u>   ◄ COMPARING

                      mad → madd + er = mad<u>der</u>

Think About   Read the examples again. Write the form of each adjective that would be used to compare three or more. _____

Apply   Read the sentences. Write comparing forms to complete them.

Maine lobsters are the _____ in the world. They are
                      fine

_____ than other lobsters. Cook them in the _____
   fat   large

pot you have. It is _____ to use a potholder than to try to do
                 safe

without. Cooked lobsters are the _____ shellfish there are.
                          red

Remember   The comparing forms of **longer adjectives** are made by using the words **more** and **most** in front of the adjectives.

Examples

	ADJECTIVE ►	beautiful	serious
	COMPARING TWO ►	more beautiful	more serious
	COMPARING MORE ►	most beautiful	most serious

Think About   Read the examples again. What word is used with a longer adjective to compare two? What word is used to compare more?

_____

Apply   Read the sentences. Write comparing forms to complete them.

Riding a horse is _____ than riding in
                          interesting

a car. It is one of the _____ ways to travel. The
                             ancient

_____ part is getting the horse to obey. The
         difficult

rider has to be _____ than the horse.
                      intelligent

Remember   Some adjectives have **special** comparing forms.

Examples

	ADJECTIVE ►	good	bad
	COMPARING TWO ►	better	worse
	COMPARING MORE ►	best	worst

Think About   Read the examples again. If you didn't know the correct forms, how could you find out? _____

Apply   Read the sentences. Write comparing forms to complete them.

It is _____ to be brave than to be a coward. But there are
         good

_____ things than refusing to fight. Fighting is the
    bad

_____ way to solve problems. The _____ person
    bad   good

doesn't always win.

Apply Read the sentences. Write the correct comparing form of the adjective that is under each line.

The _____ bike race in the world is held in Los
                    strange

Angeles. It has the _____ rules of any race. In this
                              unusual

event, the _____ bike wins. One year's winner had a
                    funny

_____ back wheel than front wheel. The front wheel was also
        big

_____ than the back wheel. It wasn't the _____
        flat   fast

bike in the race, but it was the _____ one. That gave it a
                                          crazy

_____ chance to win than just a speedy bike would have.
        good

Everyone watching agreed that this race was _____
                                                            exciting

than an ordinary one.

Apply Do some writing of your own. Tell about a funny contest you have
seen. Compare it with an ordinary contest.

_____

_____

_____

_____

REVIEW TIME

- ✔ You can use **adjectives** to **compare nouns.**

- ✔ To compare **two** nouns, you add the suffix **er** to most short adjectives. To compare **more** than two nouns, you add the suffix **est.** For some adjectives, you **change the root word** before adding the suffix.

- ✔ You use the words **more** and **most** to make the comparing forms of longer adjectives.

- ✔ For some adjectives, you use **special forms.**

When you proofread, you use special marks.

~~WORDS~~ means "Take out."   ∧ means "Add here."

Use these proofreading marks to correct the article below.

New Orleans is the older city in the state of Louisiana. The popularest

part of New Orleans is the French Quarter. That's where they have the

goodest food.

The more beautiful houses in the city are in the Garden District. The

people who built them were richest than other people.

Musicians in New Orleans play the fineest jazz in the world. Dixieland

jazz is lively than other music. Blues jazz is the sadest music in the world.

The worse thing about New Orleans is the heat. In the summer, New

Orleans is hoter than just about anywhere else.

Remember   **Suffixes** can also be used to **change** one kind of word into another.

Example   ADJECTIVE ▶   quick + ly = quick<u>ly</u>   ◀ ADVERB

Think About   Read the example again. What suffix can change an adjective into an adverb? _____

Apply   Read the sentences. Add a suffix to the adjective that is under each line to change it into an adverb. Write the adverb on the line.

Magic Johnson moves _____ across the court.
                              smooth

He bounces the ball _____ . He _____
                          soft   careful

lines up his shot. Magic talks _____ about being
                                       willing

a basketball star. He says _____ that it's hard work.
                                  frank

Remember   **Suffixes** can also be used to **change** one kind of word into another.

Examples   VERB ▶   work + er   = work<u>er</u>   ◀ NOUN
                ADJECTIVE ▶   sick   + ness = sick<u>ness</u>   ◀ NOUN

Think About   Read the examples again. What suffix can change a verb into a noun? _____ What suffix can change an adjective into a noun? _____

Apply   Read the sentences. Add a suffix to the word that is under each line to change it into a noun. Write the noun on the line.

The white-tailed jackrabbit is a _____ . It
                                         leap

can jump 20 feet with amazing _____ .
                                       quick

The meadow mouse is a _____ , too. It can
                              jump

leap 5 feet. The kangaroo rat is a _____ .
                                          kick

With great _____ , it will kick sand at a rattlesnake.
                  bold

74

Remember The suffixes **ful, less,** and **y** change a noun into an adjective.

Examples NOUN ►

help + ful = help<u>ful</u>   ◄ ADJECTIVE
thought + less = thought<u>less</u>
wind + y = wind<u>y</u>

Think About Read the examples again. What do you think each of these three suffixes means?

_____

_____

Apply Read the sentences. Add a suffix to the noun that is under each line to change it into an adjective. Write the adjective on the line. Use a dictionary if you need help.

Many American soldiers died in the _____ Vietnam War.
                                         blood

At home, some people thought that the war was _____. They
                                                      point

thought that it was _____ for our soldiers to be there. The soldiers
                         shame

who lived to come home found that they were _____.
                                                    friend

Now the dead soldiers have a memorial in Washington, D.C. It stands

all by itself on a _____ lawn. On the _____ black
                        grass   gloss

stone, there are _____ rows of names. The memorial brings
                        end

back _____ memories. But the people who see it feel more
            pain

_____ afterward.
      peace

Remember   Another way to change the meaning of a word is to add a **prefix.** A prefix is a **letter or group of letters** that is added to the **beginning** of a word.

Examples

PREFIX	MEANING	WORD
un	not, the opposite of	<u>un</u>kind
re	back, again	<u>re</u>read
mis	wrong, badly	<u>mis</u>use

Think About   What is the difference between a prefix and a suffix?

_____

_____

Apply   Read the sentences. Add a prefix to the word that is under each line. Make the word fit the meaning of the sentence. Use a dictionary if you need help.

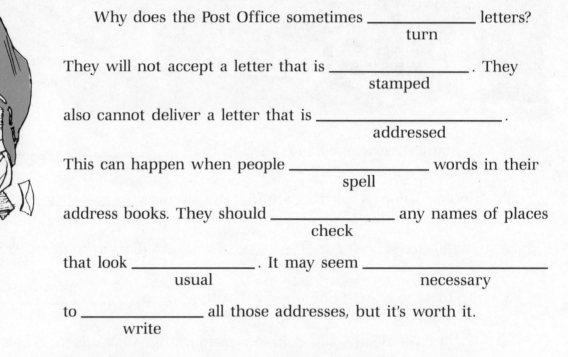

Why does the Post Office sometimes _____ letters?

turn

They will not accept a letter that is _____ . They

stamped

also cannot deliver a letter that is _____ .

addressed

This can happen when people _____ words in their

spell

address books. They should _____ any names of places

check

that look _____ . It may seem _____

usual   necessary

to _____ all those addresses, but it's worth it.

write

Apply   Do some writing of your own. Tell about a job that you had to do over.

_____

_____

_____

_____

REVIEW TIME

✔ You add a **suffix** to the **end** of a word to **change its meaning.**
Here are some examples.
- Adding **ly** changes an adjective into an adverb.
- Adding **er** changes a verb into a noun.
- Adding **ness** changes an adjective into a noun.
- Adding **ful, less,** or **y** changes a noun into an adjective.

✔ You add a **prefix** to the **beginning** of a word to **change its meaning.** Here are some examples.
- Adding **un** means "the opposite of."
- Adding **re** means "done again."
- Adding **mis** means "done wrong."

When you proofread, you use special marks.

~~WORDS~~ means "Take out."   ∧ means "Add here."

Use these proofreading marks to correct the report below.

Some fairy tales are spook and filled with sad. In these stories, the main

character is often mishappy. His or her life looks hopeness. But the

character is good and truthless. He or she acts bravey and never unbehaves.

In the end, the courage and kindly of the character are unpaid. A fairy tale

can be a good teach. Almost all of them show us that goodless pays.

WRITING TIME

Field notes are how scientists record the things they observe. Scientists look carefully at the thing they are studying. Then they write down exactly what they see. Their notes help them remember the facts and help other scientists who are studying the same thing.

Write field notes describing how two different animals behave. Make some beginning notes here to help you.

List two animals that you have watched closely.

_____

How does each animal behave?

_____

_____

How are their actions alike?

_____

_____

How are their actions different?

_____

_____

Now write a set of field notes comparing the three animals. Follow these steps.

1. Use scratch paper for your first copy. Write the whole set of field notes.

2. Show your writing to a friend. Talk about how to make it better.

3. Revise your field notes. Take out things you don't like and add new things. Use some adjectives that compare nouns. Change words to make their meaning clear.

4. Now proofread your work. Check spelling and the way you used words. Be sure you used the correct forms of words.

5. When your field notes are ready, copy them neatly onto a clean sheet of paper.

6. Share your field notes with the class.

Look at the picture of the two horses. Tell how they are alike and how they are different. Use a separate sheet of paper.

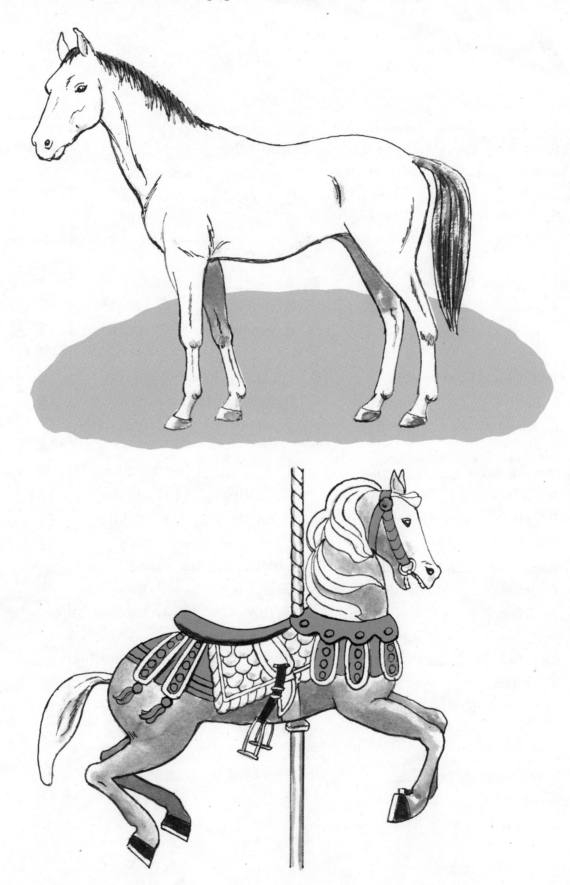

TEST TIME

Directions Read each sentence. Decide which word best completes it. Fill in the circle that has the same letter as your answer.	Sample

Sample

I have _____ a vacation.

A took   C take
B taken   D takes

Answer Column

S Ⓐ Ⓑ Ⓒ Ⓓ

---

1 I _____ out last night.

   A goes   C gone
   B go   D went

2 Gina _____ 16 years old.

   E be   G is
   F am   H are

3 The chickens _____ grain.

   A ate   C eaten
   B eats   D eated

4 Miss Rowe _____ her car.

   E drive   G drived
   F drives   H driven

5 Your hair is _____ than mine.

   A longest   C longer
   B more longer   D long

6 Troy found three _____.

   E penny   G penny's
   F pennys   H pennies

7 Jill is _____ to come.

   A reable   C misable
   B preable   D unable

8 I _____ a letter tomorrow.

   E have written   G write
   F wrote   H will write

9 The _____ played today.

   A children   C childes
   B childs   D childrens

10 I had _____ the ball.

   E threw   G thrown
   F throw   H throwed

11 Roses are the _____ beautiful flower.

   A more   C mostest
   B most   D best

12 The bird is _____.

   E flying   G flies
   F fly   H flier

Answer Column

1 Ⓐ Ⓑ Ⓒ Ⓓ
2 Ⓔ Ⓕ Ⓖ Ⓗ
3 Ⓐ Ⓑ Ⓒ Ⓓ
4 Ⓔ Ⓕ Ⓖ Ⓗ
5 Ⓐ Ⓑ Ⓒ Ⓓ
6 Ⓔ Ⓕ Ⓖ Ⓗ
7 Ⓐ Ⓑ Ⓒ Ⓓ
8 Ⓔ Ⓕ Ⓖ Ⓗ
9 Ⓐ Ⓑ Ⓒ Ⓓ
10 Ⓔ Ⓕ Ⓖ Ⓗ
11 Ⓐ Ⓑ Ⓒ Ⓓ
12 Ⓔ Ⓕ Ⓖ Ⓗ

Go on to the next page.

| Directions Read each sentence. Decide which one is correctly written. Fill in the circle that has the same letter as your answer. | Sample
A We make cake yesterday.
B We have maked cake yesterday.
C We made cake yesterday.
D We will make cake yesterday. | Answer Column
S Ⓐ Ⓑ ●Ⓒ Ⓓ |

1 A The boss was right.
B The boss were right.
C The boss are right.
D The boss been right.

2 E I will study last night.
F I have study last night.
G I study last night.
H I studied last night.

3 A Both box were heavy.
B Both boxs were heavy.
C Both boxes were heavy.
D Both box's were heavy.

4 E Sean had spoke to me.
F Sean had spoken to me.
G Sean had speaked to me.
H Sean has speaks to me.

5 A Is any animal most tallest than a giraffe?
B Is there any animal more tall than a giraffe?
C Is any animal taller than a giraffe?
D Is any animal tallest than a giraffe?

6 E Has Nan ridden in a plane?
F Has Nan rode in a plane?
G Has Nan ride in a plane?
H Has Nan rided in a plane?

7 A Bob falled down.
B Bob fallen down.
C Bob fall down.
D Bob fell down.

8 E Jeff hoping to come.
F Jeff is hoping to come.
G Jeff be hoping to come.
H Jeff hope to come.

9 A The dog try to dance.
B The dog tryed to dance.
C The dog trys to dance.
D The dog tries to dance.

10 E This is the excitingest game ever.
F This is the most excitingest game ever.
G This is the most exciting game ever.
H This is the more exciting game ever.

Answer Column

1 Ⓐ Ⓑ Ⓒ Ⓓ
2 Ⓔ Ⓕ Ⓖ Ⓗ
3 Ⓐ Ⓑ Ⓒ Ⓓ
4 Ⓔ Ⓕ Ⓖ Ⓗ
5 Ⓐ Ⓑ Ⓒ Ⓓ
6 Ⓔ Ⓕ Ⓖ Ⓗ
7 Ⓐ Ⓑ Ⓒ Ⓓ
8 Ⓔ Ⓕ Ⓖ Ⓗ
9 Ⓐ Ⓑ Ⓒ Ⓓ
10 Ⓔ Ⓕ Ⓖ Ⓗ

SENDING SIGNALS— CAPITAL LETTERS

When you write, you use **signals** to help your reader understand what you mean. **Capital letters** are one kind of signal. They are used with certain special words.

Think About   Read these sentences.

>That rose really cheers me up.
>Help me to find peanuts.
>We live on a street.

Now look at these sentences:

>That Rose really cheers me up.
>Help me to find Peanuts.
>We live on A Street.

What change has been made in each sentence?

_____

When each change was made, did the meaning of the sentence change? If so, how?

_____

_____

_____

Look at the sentences again. Think about these questions: Is Rose a flower or a particular person? Is Peanuts a food or a particular pet cat? Is A Street any street or a particular street named A? Now write your thoughts. Tell how a capital letter can change the meaning of a word.

_____

_____

Capital letters show that you are talking about something particular. They help your reader to understand exactly what you mean.

Remember The **first word of a sentence** begins with a capital letter. The pronoun **I** is always written as a capital letter, too.

Examples The Komodo dragon is a giant lizard.
If I ever see one, I will tell you about it.

Think About Read the examples again. Why is the first word of a sentence capitalized?

_____

Apply Read the sentences. Circle each word that should begin with a capital letter.

in school, i am studying Komodo dragons. they are about ten feet

long and can weigh up to 300 pounds. these lizards use their tongues for

smelling. isn't that strange? you and i, of course, use our noses for

smelling. the Komodo dragon eats deer and goats. this animal looks so

fierce that i would hate to meet one. yet i have read that the Komodo

dragon would rather hide than fight.

Apply Do some writing of your own. Tell whether you would rather hide or fight and why.

_____

_____

_____

_____

Examples <u>M</u>iss <u>F</u>lora <u>T</u>. <u>P</u>ringle   <u>B</u>oy <u>S</u>couts of <u>A</u>merica

Think About Read the examples again. Which parts of the name of a group of people are capitalized?

_____

Apply Read the sentences. Circle each word that should begin with a capital letter.

sarah winnemuca was a Native american. Her people were called the paiute. In the 1860s and 1870s, white settlers began taking their land in Nevada. sarah went to see president rutherford b. hayes to protest. Later, a law was passed giving back the land.

Many first americans have become famous. squanto helped the pilgrims through a bad winter. sequoya created an alphabet so that the cherokee could write their language. And sacajawea helped the explorers meriwether lewis and william clark as they traveled west.

Apply Do some writing of your own. Tell about another Native American.

_____

_____

_____

_____

Remember **Proper nouns** begin with a capital letter. The names of **particular places** and **animals** are proper nouns. Each main word in the name is capitalized.

Examples
<u>S</u>pot	<u>O</u>ak <u>D</u>rive	<u>A</u>tlantic <u>O</u>cean
<u>M</u>orris the <u>C</u>at	<u>S</u>eattle	<u>M</u>ount <u>W</u>hitney
	<u>M</u>ontana	<u>U</u>nited <u>S</u>tates of <u>A</u>merica

Think About Read the examples again. What kinds of words are <u>not</u> capitalized in a proper noun?

_____

Apply Read the sentences. Circle each word that should begin with a capital letter.

Mark Twain grew up in hannibal, a city on the banks of the mississippi river. After the Civil War, he crossed the rocky mountains to work at different jobs in california, nevada, and hawaii. Later, a newspaper in san francisco hired Twain to travel to europe and write about his trip. When he returned to america, he began to write the many books he is famous for. One of Twain's best known stories takes place in calaveras county. It tells of the frog jumping contest held there every year. The winners aren't the largest frogs, but the strongest. With names like thumper, champ, and long legs, they are quite a sight.

Apply Do some writing of your own. Tell about some places you have visited on a trip.

_____

_____

_____

_____

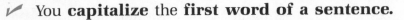

REVIEW TIME

- You **capitalize** the **first word of a sentence.**
- You **capitalize** the pronoun **I.**
- You **capitalize** each main word of a **proper noun.** This includes the names of **particular people, places,** and **animals.**

When you proofread, you use special marks.

≡ under a letter means "Make this a capital letter."

/ through a letter means "Make this a small letter."

Use these proofreading marks to correct the news report below.

james randi studied magic when he was a boy in canada. His real

name was randall j. H. zwinge, but he changed it to Amazing randi when

he became a professional Magician. Randi has performed on both sides of

the atlantic ocean. in new york City i saw him escape from a straitjacket

while he was hanging 110 feet above a famous street called broadway.

Randi doesn't believe in using magic to cheat people. in fact, he works

with dr. carl sagan and other Scientists. he has received an award for his

work from the macArthur Foundation.

Randi now lives in plantation, florida, with charlie, his Cat.

Remember   **Proper nouns** begin with a capital letter. The names of **particular things** are proper nouns. Each main word in the name is capitalized.

Examples   Saturday   First National Bank
                March   Sloat Elementary School
                Fourth of July   Barb's Bike Shop

Think About   Read the examples again. What kinds of things can have particular names?

_____

Apply   Read the sentences. Circle each word that should begin with a capital letter.

Schools are not all the same. At blue ridge middle school, students go

to class from monday to saturday. They also have a long school year.

Classes begin in august and end in june. Students have the month of july

off, along with holidays like thanksgiving and christmas.

At homewood high school, students go to class for half of the day.

The other half of the day, they work. Some are learning business at the

marsh company. Others are learning about computers at techno,

incorporated. Still other students are learning about government at the

department of housing.

Apply   Do some writing of your own. Tell what you think the very best school would be like.

_____

_____

_____

_____

_____

Remember An **abbreviation** is a **short way to write a word.** Usually a period (.) comes after it. If the abbreviation stands for a **proper noun,** it begins with a capital letter. In United States Postal Service abbreviations for states, both letters are capitals, and there is no period.

Examples

Jackson Avenue	King Company	Thursday	Ohio
Jackson <u>A</u>ve.	King <u>C</u>o.	<u>T</u>hurs.	<u>OH</u>

Think About Read the examples again. When are abbreviations for words like **avenue** and **company** capitalized?

_____

Apply Read the groups of words. Circle the abbreviation in each one that should begin with a capital letter.

1. a store on First st.

2. a party on nov. 19

3. mrs. Lacey's cat

4. a house in Alton, il

5. see you on mon.

6. a visit to phila.

7. grandparents in eng.

8. salmon in the Columbia r.

9. snow on mt. Hamilton

10. Mr. W.E. Walters, jr.

Apply Do some writing of your own. Tell about some of the people and places you visited on three different days last week. Use abbreviations.

_____
_____
_____
_____
_____
_____

Remember   The **first word,** the **last word,** and **each main word** in the **title of a work** begin with a capital letter. This includes titles of books, stories, poems, songs, and radio or TV shows.

Examples   BOOK ► *Little House on the Prairie*
STORY ► "The Gift of the Magi"
POEM ► "Stopping by Woods on a Snowy Evening"
SONG ► "Puff the Magic Dragon"
SHOW ► "Who's the Boss?"

Think About   Read the examples again. When are words like *the* and *a* capitalized in a title?

_____

Apply   Read the sentences. Circle each word that should begin with a capital letter.

There's a lot of work to do when you camp out. But it's worth it when you get to sit around the campfire after dinner. You sing songs like "there was an old lady who swallowed a fly" and "row, row, row your boat." You tell scary stories like "the pit and the pendulum" or "the fall of the house of usher." Sometimes you remember poems like "miss t." from Walter de la Mare's book *come hither.* It's even fun just to retell stories from favorite TV shows like "star trek" or "tales from the crypt." Then you go off to your sleeping bag for a long night's rest.

Apply   Do some writing of your own. Write the title of your favorite book.

_____

Write the title of your favorite TV show.

_____

Write the title of the song you like best right now.

_____

89

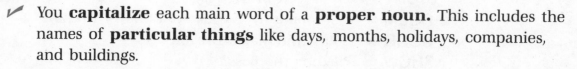

✔ You **capitalize** each main word of a **proper noun.** This includes the names of **particular things** like days, months, holidays, companies, and buildings.

✔ You **capitalize abbreviations** that stand for proper nouns.

✔ You **capitalize** the **first word,** the **last word,** and **each main word** in the titles of works.

When you proofread, you use special marks.

≡ under a letter means "Make this a capital letter."

/ through a letter means "Make this a small letter."

Use these proofreading marks to correct the article below.

Our teacher, mrs. Santini, writes books for children. Her publisher is Kidtales co. Their address is 457 First st., Frankfort, ky. On fri., mar. 25, MRS. Santini took our class to visit her publisher. The people there showed us how books are made. They were working on a book called *jamie And the Space boy.*

The designer, mr. wong, decides how the book is going to look. He works with the artist, MR. Newell c. Post. When everything is ready, the book will be sent to Los angeles to be printed.

Our teacher is writing a short story called "let's go, gang." She is also writing a poem called "a Special day." Next mon., apr. 4, she is going to be on TV on "people are talking."

WRITING TIME

A **research report** tells facts and information about a particular topic. You use an **outline** to take notes.

Choose a subject to write about. Read and fill in the information below. Write other interesting facts on another piece of paper. List the books you used as sources.

Person's Name _____

I. Personal Facts

   A. Dates lived _____

   B. Birthplace _____

II. Early years

   A. Parents _____

   B. Interests _____

III. Work

   A. Education _____

   B. Job _____

   C. Famous for _____

   D. Awards _____

Sources _____

Now write your research report. Follow these steps.

1. Use scratch paper for your first copy. Write the whole job report.

2. Show your writing to a friend. Talk about how to make it better.

3. Revise your report. Take out things you don't like and add new things.

4. Now proofread your work. Check your spelling, your capitalization, and punctuation.

5. When your report is ready, copy it neatly onto a clean sheet of paper.

6. Share your job report with the class.

TEST TIME

Directions Read each sentence. Decide which word is written the wrong way. Fill in the circle that has the same letter as your answer.

Samples

Did you see mrs. Daly?
 A   B   C   D

I read *Treasure island.*
 E   F   G   H

Answer Column

S Ⓐ Ⓑ Ⓒ Ⓓ
  Ⓔ Ⓕ Ⓖ Ⓗ

1 Kathy lives on Maple st.
     A   B   C   D

8 Does nancy have red hair?
      E   F   G   H

2 Call me on wednesday.
     E   F   G   H

9 The Monkey got loose.
     A   B   C   D

3 Wayne and i did it.
     A   B C D

10 I live in kansas City.
      E F   G   H

4 Have you been to idaho?
     E   F   G   H

11 My dentist is dr. Ho.
      A   B   C   D

5 *Ramona the pest* is a good book.
            A   B   C   D

12 What day is halloween?
      E   F   G   H

6 Thanksgiving is in november.
         E   F G   H

13 my birthday is Jan. 1.
      A   B   C   D

7 Take the Bus to the city.
     A   B   C   D

14 Please give taffy a bone.
      E   F   G   H

1 Ⓐ Ⓑ Ⓒ Ⓓ
2 Ⓔ Ⓕ Ⓖ Ⓗ
3 Ⓐ Ⓑ Ⓒ Ⓓ
4 Ⓔ Ⓕ Ⓖ Ⓗ
5 Ⓐ Ⓑ Ⓒ Ⓓ
6 Ⓔ Ⓕ Ⓖ Ⓗ
7 Ⓐ Ⓑ Ⓒ Ⓓ
8 Ⓔ Ⓕ Ⓖ Ⓗ
9 Ⓐ Ⓑ Ⓒ Ⓓ
10 Ⓔ Ⓕ Ⓖ Ⓗ
11 Ⓐ Ⓑ Ⓒ Ⓓ
12 Ⓔ Ⓕ Ⓖ Ⓗ
13 Ⓐ Ⓑ Ⓒ Ⓓ
14 Ⓔ Ⓕ Ⓖ Ⓗ

Go on to the next page.

Sample

A I live in Salt Lake City.
B i live in Salt Lake City.
C I live in salt lake city.
D I live in Salt lake city.

Answer Column
S Ⓐ Ⓑ Ⓒ Ⓓ

1
A I stayed up new year's eve.
B i stayed up new year's eve.
C I stayed up New Year's Eve.
D i stayed up New Year's Eve.

6
E That's sen. Paul t. Kim.
F That's Sen. Paul T. Kim.
G That's Sen. paul t. Kim.
H That's sen. paul t. Kim.

2
E My sister's name is Noelle.
F My Sister's name is Noelle.
G My Sister's name is Noelle.
H My sister's name is noelle.

7
A "Easy rider" is a song.
B "Easy Rider" is a song.
C "Easy Rider" is a Song.
D "easy rider" is a song.

3
A We visited Beverly, mass.
B We visited beverly, mass.
C We visited Beverly, Mass.
D We visited beverly, Mass.

8
E mr. a. g. blake lives here.
F Mr. a. g. blake lives here.
G Mr. a. g. Blake lives here.
H Mr. A. G. Blake lives here.

4
E I just read *Lad, a Dog.*
F I just read *Lad, a dog.*
G I just read *lad, a dog.*
H I just read *Lad, A Dog.*

9
A I work in York, pa.
B I work in york, pa.
C i work in York, Pa.
D I work in York, Pa.

5
A talk to aunt Jane.
B Talk to aunt jane.
C talk to Aunt jane.
D Talk to Aunt Jane.

10
E Today is tues., march 1.
F Today is tues., March 1.
G Today is Tues., March 1.
H Today is Tues., march 1.

Answer Column
1 Ⓐ Ⓑ Ⓒ Ⓓ
2 Ⓔ Ⓕ Ⓖ Ⓗ
3 Ⓐ Ⓑ Ⓒ Ⓓ
4 Ⓔ Ⓕ Ⓖ Ⓗ
5 Ⓐ Ⓑ Ⓒ Ⓓ
6 Ⓔ Ⓕ Ⓖ Ⓗ
7 Ⓐ Ⓑ Ⓒ Ⓓ
8 Ⓔ Ⓕ Ⓖ Ⓗ
9 Ⓐ Ⓑ Ⓒ Ⓓ
10 Ⓔ Ⓕ Ⓖ Ⓗ

STOP

Sending Signals— Punctuation Marks

When you write, you use **signals** to help your reader understand what you mean. **Punctuation marks** are one kind of signal. You use them at the end of sentences and in other special places.

Think About   Look at these traffic signals. What do they tell you?

These signals tell you things that you need to know as you are driving along. They say: "Stop here!" "Slow down here!" "This is what's coming next!"

Why do we have traffic signals? What would happen if we didn't have them?

_____

_____

Punctuation marks are like traffic signals. They tell your readers things that they need to know. Look at these punctuation marks:

. (period)   , (comma)   " " (quotation marks)

Which punctuation mark says, "Stop here!"? _____

Which one says, "Slow down!"? _____

Which one says, "This is what's coming next!"? _____

Why do we have punctuation marks? What would happen if we didn't?

_____

_____

Punctuation marks tell your reader how to "read" your writing.

Remember Some **punctuation marks** signal the **end** of a sentence. A **period (.)** ends a **declarative** or **imperative** sentence. A **question mark (?)** ends an **interrogative** sentence. An **exclamation point (!)** ends an **exclamatory** sentence or an **imperative** sentence that shows strong feeling.

Examples Some trees lose their leaves in the fall.
Look at that bare oak tree.
Why don't pine trees lose their leaves?
How sharp their needles are!
Be careful when you touch them!

Think About Read the examples again. Why can two different punctuation marks end an imperative sentence?

_____

Apply Read the sentences. End each one with the correct punctuation mark.

Some animals have babies that look just like them Think about a puppy Doesn't it look just like a grown-up dog, only smaller

Is this true of all animals Take a look at a caterpillar Its mother was a butterfly or a moth How different these two creatures are

Do you know what a tadpole is It's a baby frog, but it looks like a fish until its legs grow and its tail disappears Watch out This one is almost ready to jump How much it has changed in just a few weeks

Apply Do some writing of your own. Tell about another animal whose babies <u>do</u> look like it. Vary the kinds of sentences you use.

_____

_____

_____

95

Remember   A **period (.)** is used after **initials** and most **abbreviations.**

Examples   Dr. S. T. Diaz   Rider Rd.   Mon.   L. Ontario

Think About   Read the examples again. What does the period after an initial or an abbreviation signal?

_____

Apply   Read the groups of words. Rewrite each one, using an initial or abbreviation for each underlined word. Use a dictionary if you need help.

1. 743 <u>West</u> Pine <u>Avenue</u>   _____

2. Star Paper <u>Company</u>   _____

3. <u>Mount</u> McKinley   _____

4. <u>Mister</u> <u>Elmer</u> Jones   _____

5. <u>Thursday</u>, <u>January</u> 22   _____

6. Sacramento <u>River</u>   _____

7. Juarez, <u>Mexico</u>   _____

8. <u>Captain</u> Betsy <u>Elaine</u> Richards   _____

9. <u>Post</u> <u>Office</u> Box 999   _____

10. 5 Clipper <u>Street</u>, <u>Apartment</u> 7   _____

Apply   Do some writing of your own. Use initials and abbreviations to give facts about yourself. Here are some ideas: your name, your parents' names, your address, today's day and date.

_____

_____

_____

_____

_____

REVIEW TIME

- ✔ You use a **period** to end a **declarative** or **imperative** sentence.
- ✔ You use a **question mark** to end an **interrogative** sentence.
- ✔ You use an **exclamation point** to end an **exclamatory** sentence or an **imperative** sentence that shows strong feeling.
- ✔ You use a **period** after **initials** and most **abbreviations** to show that letters are missing.

When you proofread, you use special marks.

⋀ means "Add here." You use it to put in a question mark or exclamation point.

⊙ means "Add a period here."

Use these proofreading marks to correct the letter below.

---

808 S Rendell Dr

S F , CA 94124

Aug 4, 1990

Dear Mrs Lang,

What a trip this has been We have really enjoyed our visit to St Louis Did you know the city was once French Pres Thomas Jefferson bought it in 1803

The center of the city lies between the Mississippi R and 15th St That's where the U S Courthouse is From Washington Ave you can cross the Eads Bridge to East St Louis Then you're in Ill , not Missouri

Please tell everyone that we'll be back this Sat Be ready to look at some pictures What a lot of them we took

Your friend,

Jenny

Remember   A **comma (,)** is used to separate things. It separates the **day** from the **year** in a **date.**

Examples   October 26, 1985
On October 26, 1985, Hurricane Juan hit the Florida coast.

Think About   Read the examples again. When a date is used in a sentence, a second comma is needed. What does it separate?

Apply   Read the sentences. Add commas where they belong.

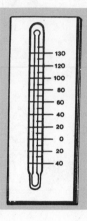

Almost every state has hot weather sometimes. July 4 1911 was Vermont's hottest day. The temperature was 105°. Virginia reached 110° on July 15 1954. Hawaii has never been that hot. Its highest temperature was 100° on April 27 1931 at Pohala. Even Alaska has been that warm. The date was June 27 1915. America's hottest day ever was recorded in California. On July 10 1913 the temperature in Death Valley hit 134°.

Remember   A **comma (,)** separates the name of a **city** from the name of a **state** or **country.**

Examples   Memphis, Tennessee
Memphis, Tennessee, has six TV stations.

Think About   Read the examples again. A second comma is needed in the sentence. What does it separate?

Apply   Read the sentences. Add commas where they belong.

Tennis has been around for over 100 years. Wimbledon England was the home of the first big championship in 1877. An American named Mary Outerbridge brought the sport to New York City New York in 1874. The first U.S. championship was held in Newport Rhode Island in 1881. Now the event is held in Flushing Meadow New York. A third big championship takes place each year in Paris France.

Remember   A **comma (,)** separates the **name of a person being spoken to** from the rest of a sentence.

Examples   Liz, what time is it?
I've lost my watch, Rachel.

Think About   Read the examples again. When does the comma come after the person's name? When does it come before?

_____

_____

Apply   Think of friends you like to talk to. Write their names in this conversation. Then add commas where they belong.

_____ do you know the names of the parts of your house?

Of course I do _____!

Then what is the highest part of the roof called _____?

_____ do you know?

It's called the roof tree _____.

Remember   A **comma (,)** separates words like **yes, no, well,** and **however** from the rest of a sentence.

Examples   Yes, Charles Babbage planned the first computer.
However, his machine was never built.

Think About   Read the examples again. Where are words like **yes, no,** and **well** used in a sentence?

_____

Apply   Write **yes, no, well,** or **however** to complete each sentence. Then add commas where they belong.

_____ I'll bet you've never heard of a fishing cat.

_____ I haven't. Have you?

_____ I've seen them in pictures of Africa.

_____ I don't know how these special cats can swim.

_____ maybe they have webs between their toes, like ducks.

Examples   Men, women, and children can become martial artists.
They learn to kick, punch, or throw their opponents.
Martial artists are calm, sure, and polite.

Think About   Read the examples again. Where are commas placed in a series?

_____

Apply   Read the sentences. Add commas where they belong.

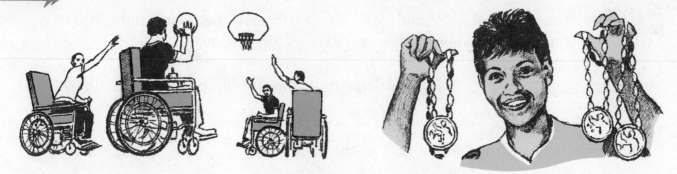

When he was nine, Ron Scanlon was in an accident that broke his back. People thought he would never again work play sports or do much of anything. But Ron was tough determined and ready to learn. He mastered wheelchair football wheelchair basketball and kung fu.

Wilma Rudolph is another person who beat the odds. Doctors checked her leg talked over the problem and decided she would never be able to use it again. But Wilma's mother brothers and sisters would not give up. Every day they rubbed her leg helped her move it and encouraged her. Before long, Wilma was walking running and even playing basketball. She went on to win Olympic gold medals in track.

Apply   Do some writing of your own. Tell about a time you did something that no one else thought you could do.

_____

_____

_____

_____

Remember   A **comma (,)** separates the two main parts of a **compound sentence.**

Examples   Forests help clean air, and oceans cool it.
Swamps have lots of water, but deserts have very little.
We must take care of all the earth's areas, or they might disappear.

Think About   Read the examples again. What word comes after the comma in a compound sentence? _____

Apply   Read the sentences. Add commas where they belong.

Tortoises live on land and they cannot swim. Turtles live in water but they lay their eggs on land. These creatures can be brown or they can be brightly colored. Some turtles live in sea water but others like fresh water better. The sea turtles have flippers and the fresh-water turtles have short legs with webbed feet. You can look for fresh-water turtles in ponds or you can find them in swamps. These animals move slowly and they can only protect themselves by hiding. They may pull into their shells or they may dive deep under the water. Turtles can live up to 100 years but many of the bigger ones are being killed off by people.

Apply   Do some writing of your own. Tell something you know about tortoises or turtles.

_____

_____

_____

_____

REVIEW TIME

✔ You use a **comma** to separate:
- the **day** from the **year** in a **date**
- the **date** from the **rest of a sentence**
- the name of a **city** from the name of a **state** or **country**
- the name of the **state** or **country** from the **rest of a sentence**
- the words **yes, no, well,** and **however** from the rest of a sentence
- the **name of the person being spoken to** from the rest of a sentence
- words in a **series**
- the two main parts of a **compound sentence**

When you proofread, you use special marks.

⌃ means "Add a comma."

Use this proofreading mark to correct the message below.

Sally this is what to do if you are ever in an accident. I was in one once and I know it can be very frightening. It was on June 1 1990. Mom and I were driving home from Tulsa Oklahoma when we were hit by a speeding car. Well we were lucky. Our car turned over but we had our seatbelts fastened. We were bruised shaken and scared. The police came took our names and filed a report. Yes Mom's insurance company paid for everything. By June 15 1990 the car was as good as new. If you're ever in an accident, keep calm Sally. That's the best thing to do.

Remember   An **apostrophe (')** is a signal that is used within words. It can take the place of the letter or letters that are left out of **contractions.**

Examples   we will   could not   she would   I am
                we'll   couldn't   she'd   I'm

Think About   Read the examples again. What is a contraction made of?

_____

Apply   Read the sentences. Write a contraction for the words that are under each line.

Paper money _____ all alike. In our country, for example, dollar
                          is not

bills _____ brightly colored. _____ green and gray. Yet
      are not   They are

in France, _____ find pink, blue, and yellow money.
           you will

Other countries _____ have coins like ours, either. In Ireland,
                 do not

_____ got beautiful animals on their coins. _____ got
they have   We have

pictures of presidents on most of ours.

U.S. money _____ always looked the way it does now.
           has not

_____ changed over the years. People today probably _____
It has   would not

recognize some of our earlier bills and coins.

Apply   Do some writing of your own. Tell what you use money for.

_____

_____

_____

Remember An **apostrophe (')** is used to make a noun **possessive.** The possessive form of a **singular** noun is made by adding the **apostrophe** and **s.**

Examples the creature's skin   the child's toy

Think About Read the examples again. If a noun ends in **s,** how can you tell whether it is plural or possessive?

_____

Apply Read the sentences. Write the possessive form of the noun that is under each line.

A _____ tools are a level, a hammer, and a
       carpenter

saw. Different kinds of wrenches are a _____ tools. A
                           plumber

_____ tools are bandages and thermometers. A _____
  nurse   cook

tools are pots and pans. What are a _____ tools?
                                         student

Remember For **plural** nouns that end in **s,** just the **apostrophe** is added to make the **possessive** form.

Examples the wolves' den   the girls' dresses

Think About Read the examples again. If the noun is plural and ends in **s,** how can you tell whether it is possessive?

_____

Apply Read the sentences. Write the possessive form of the noun that is under each line.

Pencils and paper are _____ tools. _____
                           teachers   Coaches

tools are footballs and basketballs. _____ tools are
                                          Secretaries

typewriters or computers. _____ tools are their
                                  Bus drivers

buses. What would you say are _____ tools?
                                     parents

Remember   The **possessive** form of **plural** nouns that **do not end** in **s** is made the same way as a singular possessive form.

Examples   the women's jobs   the deer's antlers

Think About   Read the examples again. What is added to make these possessive forms? _____

Apply   Read the sentences. Write the possessive form of the noun that is under each line.

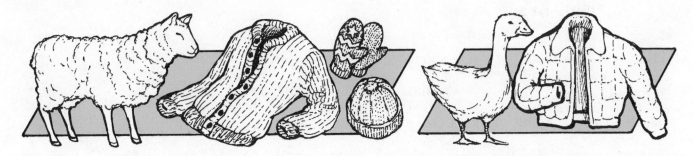

_____ wool is very soft and warm. It is used to make
        Sheep

_____ sweaters. It is used for _____ clothes, too. In
    women   men

addition, _____ mittens and hats are often made from
                    children

wool. Other animals help clothe us, too. If you have a down jacket, it is

filled with _____ feathers. But some creatures like to use
                  geese

_____ warm clothes. I have seen old clothes used for
      people

_____ nests.
    mice

Apply   Do some writing of your own. Tell about other materials we use for clothes.

_____

_____

_____

_____

105

✔ You use an **apostrophe** to take the place of letters left out of **contractions.**

✔ You use an **apostrophe** to form **possessive** nouns. You add an **apostrophe** plus **s** to a **singular** noun or a **plural noun that does not end in s.** You add just an **apostrophe to a plural noun** that **ends in s.**

When you proofread, you use special marks.

᠅ means "Add an apostrophe."

Use this proofreading mark to correct the story below.

Wouldnt you like to know what each bird eats? Look at its beak. Birds

beaks tell us a lot. A hummingbirds beak is long and thin so that it can

suck juice from flowers. Pelicans beaks look like pouches, dont they?

Thats so the pelican can carry a lot of fish. An eagles beak is very

powerful. The eagle uses it to catch mice.

Canaries and parakeets are childrens pets. Canaries beaks are thick

and strong so they can crack open seeds. A parakeets beak is the same

way.

Remember   **Conversation** is what people say to one another. It is written in a special way. The exact words being spoken are called a **direct quotation. Quotation marks (" ")** are used before and after them. A **comma (,)** comes before the quotation marks. It separates the direct quotation from conversation words like **said, asked,** and **answered.**

Examples   Miss Harper asked, "Who was Laura Ingalls Wilder?"
Emily answered, "She was a famous writer."

Think About   Read the examples again. Why do you think quotation marks are needed in writing?

Apply   Read the conversation. Add quotation marks and commas where they belong.

Melody stated I like to read about pioneers.

Emily told her You should read The *Little House on the Prairie.*

Melody asked Is that a book by Laura Ingalls Wilder?

Emily answered Yes, it's my favorite.

Tony grumbled Why did she write only about pioneers?

Emily replied She was a pioneer herself.

Miss Harper explained She wrote about growing up in Nebraska in the 1800s.

Melody added Many settlers moved there to get free land.

Miss Harper agreed Yes, and then the railroad came, and even more people moved west.

Emily exclaimed I wish I could have lived back then!

▶ **Remember** A **direct quotation** is like a sentence within a sentence. The **first word** begins with a **capital letter.** The correct **end punctuation** comes **before** the final quotation marks.

▶ **Examples**   Todd shouted, "Watch out!"
Amy asked, "What's wrong?"
Todd answered, "There's a bee right beside your head."

▶ **Think About**   Read the examples again. Why do the end punctuation marks come before the final quotation marks?

▶ **Apply**   Read the conversation. Circle each word that should begin with a capital letter. Add the correct end punctuation marks.

LeVal said, "mom is giving blood, and I'm going with her "

Mike cried out, "what a scarey thing to do "

Clare said, "don't be silly, Mike "

LeVal explained, "the blood bank needs blood for people who are in

the hospital "

Clare added, "what do you think would happen if nobody gave any "

Mike answered, "people would die, I guess "

Clare said, "just think how it would feel to save somebody's life "

LeVal exclaimed, "how great that would be "

Mike asked, "who invented blood banks "

LeVal answered, "it was a black doctor named Charles Drew "

Remember In written conversation, a **new paragraph** is begun each time the **speaker changes.**

Example   Enrico asked, "What kind of work does your father do?"
          Heather answered, "He's a harbor pilot."

Think About Read the example again. What **two** things show the reader that the speaker has changed?

_____

_____

Apply Read the conversation. Write it correctly on the lines below. Indent to start a new paragraph whenever the speaker changes. Add correct capitalization and punctuation.

Heather explained harbor pilots guide big ships into busy harbors Enrico asked is it a difficult job Heather said imagine trying to guide a ship through heavy traffic in a bad storm Enrico asked why doesn't the captain of the ship guide it Heather answered each harbor is different, and the harbor pilot learns all about it Enrico said oh, I see

_____

_____

_____

_____

_____

_____

_____

_____

_____

REVIEW TIME

✔ You write **conversation** in a special way.

- You put **quotation marks** before and after a **direct quotation.**
- You use a **comma** to separate a direct quotation from the conversation words.
- You use a **capital letter** to begin a **direct quotation.**
- You use a **period, a question mark,** or an **exclamation point** to end a direct quotation.
- You begin a **new paragraph** each time the speaker changes.

When you proofread, you use special marks.

∧ means "Add here." You use it to add a question mark or an exclamation point.

≡ under a letter means "Make this a capital letter."

⊙ means "Add a period." ∧ means "Add a comma."

❝ ❞ means "Add quotation marks." ⧉ means "Start a new paragraph."

Use these proofreading marks to correct the conversation below.

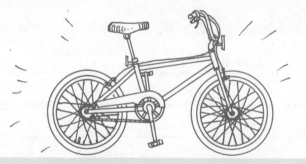

Brad exclaimed wow, what a great new bike that is " Christy said isn't it super Brad asked, Why are the wheels so big Christy explained it's a mountain bike for dirt trails." Brad asked "why does it have gears like a racing bike " Christy answered sometimes people use mountain bikes for racing. Brad said will you let me try it out? Christy said You can give it a try right after I do

WRITING TIME

An **interview** is a way to get information. You choose a person who knows a lot about a particular subject. Then you ask that person questions. Newspaper reporters get a lot of their information by interviewing people.

Do an interview of your own. Make some notes to help you.

Pick a classmate to interview. What subject does this person know a lot about? It could be a sport, a hobby, or a book that person has read. Write the person's name and the subject here.

_____

What several questions that you would like to ask about this subject.

1. _____

2. _____

3. _____

4. _____

5. _____

Interview the person and write down the answers to your questions.

Now write your interview. Include an interesting part of your conversation in your writing. Write each question you asked, and then write the person's answer. Use quotation marks and conversation words. Follow these steps.

1. Use scratch paper for your first copy. Write the whole interview.

2. Show your writing to a friend. Talk about how to make it better.

3. Revise your interview. Take out things you don't like and add new things.

4. Now proofread your work. Check your spelling, capitalization, and punctuation.

5. When your interview is ready, copy it neatly onto a clean sheet of paper.

6. Share your interview with the class.

Look at the picture of the carnival. Describe what you see happening in it. What do you think the people are saying to one another? Write their conversation on a separate sheet of paper.

►►► TEST TIME

Directions Read each sentence. Look for the line that has a mistake in **punctuation.** Fill in the circle that has the same letter as that line. If there are no mistakes, fill in the fourth circle.	**Sample** A Shauna where are B you going in C such a hurry? D (No mistakes)	**Answer Column** S Ⓐ Ⓑ Ⓒ Ⓓ

1
A My little sister
B was born on
C April 24 1990.
D (No mistakes)

2
E Dr Bill Palmer
F takes care of
G my whole family.
H (No mistakes)

3
A Norm exclaimed,
B the name of
C Sherrys dog.
D (No mistakes)

4
E Bees build hives,
F and they also
G make honey.
H (No mistakes)

5
A Norm explained,
B "What a cold
C day it is"
D (No mistakes)

6
E We are going
F with Sharon Jimmy
G and Roberto.
H (No mistakes)

7
A I cant remember
B where I left
C my umbrella.
D (No mistakes)

8
E Do you know
F the answer to
G this problem
H (No mistakes)

Answer Column

1 Ⓐ Ⓑ Ⓒ Ⓓ
2 Ⓔ Ⓕ Ⓖ Ⓗ
3 Ⓐ Ⓑ Ⓒ Ⓓ
4 Ⓔ Ⓕ Ⓖ Ⓗ
5 Ⓐ Ⓑ Ⓒ Ⓓ
6 Ⓔ Ⓕ Ⓖ Ⓗ
7 Ⓐ Ⓑ Ⓒ Ⓓ
8 Ⓔ Ⓕ Ⓖ Ⓗ

Go on to the next page.

9
  A Mr. Ellis asked,
  B Who is going on
  C the field trip?"
  D (No mistakes)

10
  E Is Atlanta, Georgia
  F the largest city
  G in the South?
  H (No mistakes)

11
  A Teresa stated,
  B "No one can go
  C into my room."
  D (No mistakes)

12
  E Please turn
  F down the
  G radio Carly.
  H (No mistakes)

13
  A Yes I always
  B take cans back
  C to the store.
  D (No mistakes)

14
  E Sandy yelled "Hit
  F the ball out
  G of the park!"
  H (No mistakes)

15
  A Do you shop
  B at the boys
  C clothing store?
  D (No mistakes)

16
  E Fish, meat, and
  F eggs are in the
  G same food group
  H (No mistakes)

17
  A Mom let me
  B help at the
  C women's lunch.
  D (No mistakes)

18
  E Wolves live in
  F packs and they
  G work together.
  H (No mistakes)

9 (A) (B) (C) (D)
10 (E) (F) (G) (H)
11 (A) (B) (C) (D)
12 (E) (F) (G) (H)
13 (A) (B) (C) (D)
14 (E) (F) (G) (H)
15 (A) (B) (C) (D)
16 (E) (F) (G) (H)
17 (A) (B) (C) (D)
18 (E) (F) (G) (H)

CHOOSING WORDS

When you speak or write, you have to **choose the words** you want to use. Knowing about words can help you to make the best choices.

Think About   Look at these words. What do you notice about them?

happy   cheerful   glad   joyful   merry   joyous

These words mean almost the same thing.

Suppose you want to describe how you feel when things are going well. Which one of these words would you choose? Why?

_____

_____

Think of a time when you might use one of the other words. Describe it here.

_____

_____

How many words can you think of that mean "sad"? List them.

_____

_____

Which one of these words do you use most often? Why?

_____

_____

Think of a time when you might use one of the other words. Why?

_____

_____

There are many reasons for choosing one word instead of another. The more you know about words, the more choices you will have.

Remember   **Synonyms** are words that have **almost the same meaning.** They are useful for saying the same thing in different ways.

Examples   strange — odd   shout — yell   car — automobile

Think About   Read the examples again. How are the words in each pair alike?

Apply   Use synonyms to make these sentences more interesting. Cross out the repeated word and write a synonym above it. Use words from the box to help you or think of your own.

ancient	dog	silently	gazed
courageous	relatives	knew	return

Odysseus was a brave Greek hero. He had many brave adventures. This hero had a young hound named Argus, which was his favorite hound. Odysseus said good-bye to his family and went away to fight in the Trojan War. He left Argus in the care of his family.

Odysseus didn't come back for 19 years. When he finally did come back, he was in disguise. Nobody recognized him except Argus. His dog recognized him immediately. Argus was an old dog by then. He was so old that he couldn't even walk. Odysseus looked at his old hound. Argus looked at his master. The pet quietly raised his head. Then he quietly wagged his tail, laid down, and died.

116

Remember **Antonyms** are words that have **opposite meanings.** They are useful for comparing things.

Examples tight — loose   friend — enemy   stop — start

Think About Read the examples again. How are the words in each pair different?

_____

Apply Write antonyms to complete the comparing sentences. Use words from the box or think of your own.

beautiful	wet	warm	few
slowly	harmless	strong	intelligent

Some people think snakes are dangerous, but most snakes are really

_____. They are not _____ at all. In fact,

snakes are quite stupid. Their blood is cold rather than _____, and

their skin is dry, not _____ and slimy. Snakes have a great many bones,

not just a _____. They are _____, not weak. Sometimes they

move _____, but they can move very quickly when they have to.

Some people think snakes are ugly, but I think they're _____.

Apply Do some writing of your own. Use antonyms to compare two kinds of animals.

_____

_____

_____

_____

_____

_____

Remember   **Homophones** are words that **sound alike** but are **spelled differently** and have **different meanings.** It is important to choose the word that fits your meaning.

Example   <u>Eight</u> children <u>ate</u> lunch together.

Think About   Read the example again. Look at the two words that are underlined. What is the same about them? What is not the same?

_____

_____

Apply   Read the sentences. Write the correct homophones to complete them.

Have you ever ridden on a ferry? You stay _____ _____
                                                          in/inn   you're/your

car and just drive on _____ . The ship full of cars _____
                                  board/bored   sales/sails

_____ across the water. When you reach land, you drive off the ship
  right/write

and get back on the _____ . My family _____ the trip across Puget
                              rode/road   made/maid

Sound. It is _____ miles across, from the city of Seattle to Bainbridge
                    ate/eight

Island. Chief Seattle is buried not far from _____ . _____ only a
                                                              their/there   Its/It's

30-minute trip.

Remember **Homographs** are words that are **spelled alike** but have **different meanings** and may **sound different.**

Example I can't <u>bear</u> to see a <u>bear</u> in a cage.

Think About Read the example again. How are homographs different from homophones?

_____

Apply Read each sentence. Then read the meanings that the underlined homograph can have. Circle the meaning that the word has in the sentence.

1. Plant your rosebushes where they will get plenty of <u>light</u>.

    a) brightness   b) not heavy

2. Feed them <u>well</u>.

    a) a source of water   b) thoroughly

3. Rake up the dry <u>leaves</u> and burn them.

    a) the plural of *leaf*   b) goes away

4. Pests can <u>hide</u> in all sorts of places.

    a) stay out of sight   b) an animal's skin

5. <u>Watch</u> out for little brown bugs.

    a) a small clock worn on the wrist   b) look carefully

6. <u>Spray</u> them with the hose.

    a) shoot water at   b) a branch of flowers

7. Don't forget to <u>pick</u> the roses.

    a) a tool for digging   b) gather

Apply Do some writing of your own. Tell about a plant you have grown.

_____

_____

_____

_____

REVIEW TIME

- ✔ You use **synonyms**, which have **almost the same meaning,** to make your writing more interesting.

- ✔ You use **antonyms**, which have **opposite meanings,** to compare things.

- ✔ You have to be careful with **homophones** because they **sound alike** but have **different spellings** and **meanings.**

- ✔ You use **homographs,** which are words that are **spelled alike** but have **more than one meaning,** in different ways.

When you proofread, you use special marks.

~~WORDS~~ means "Take out."   ∧ means "Add here."

Use these proofreading marks to correct the article below. Replace repeated words with synonyms. Make sure that the correct homophones have been chosen.

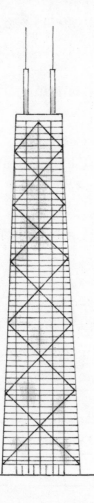

The John Hancock Building in Chicago is very tall. It is 1,127 feet, or over 100 stories, tall. Many people live in the John Hancock Building. The people who live on the top floors live above the clouds. Those people can sea the son when it's raining down below. The views from the top of the John Hancock Building are beautiful. You look out over beautiful Lake Michigan. Their are many good restaurants in the John Hancock Building. They're are many good stores and markets in it, to. People who live in the building don't ever need to go outside because everything they need is write there.

Remember **Subject pronouns** and **object pronouns** are used in different ways.

Example Natalie delivers groceries to Mrs. Yakudo.
<u>She</u> also unpacks <u>them</u> for <u>her</u>.
▲   ▲   ▲
SUBJECT   OBJECT
PRONOUN   PRONOUNS

Think About Read the examples again. How are subject pronouns used?

_____

How are object pronouns used?

_____

Apply Read the sentences. Write the correct pronouns to complete them.

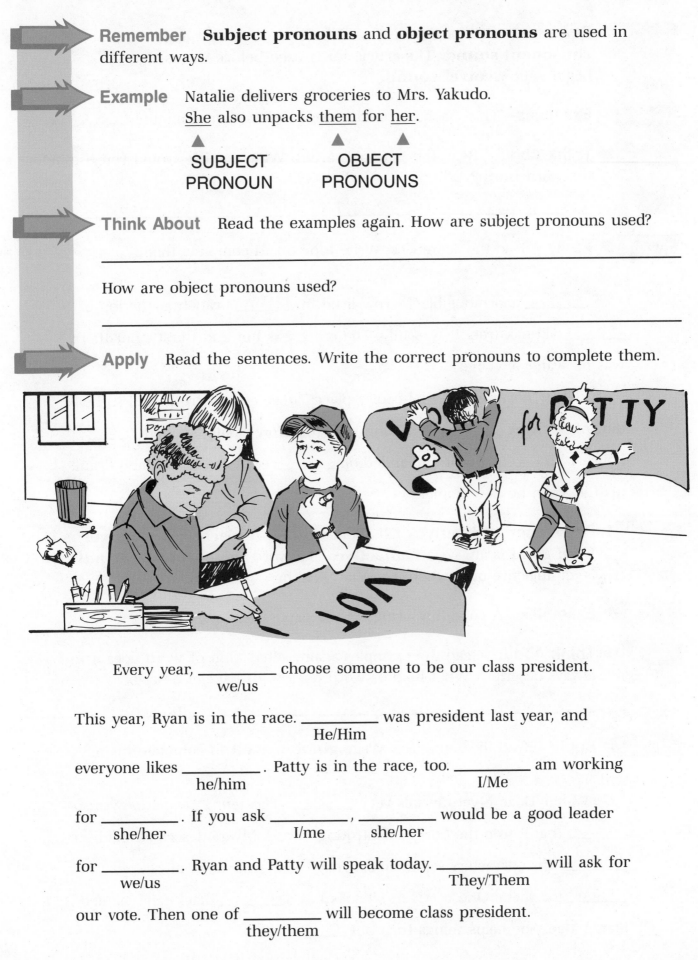

Every year, _____ choose someone to be our class president.
              we/us

This year, Ryan is in the race. _____ was president last year, and
                                  He/Him

everyone likes _____. Patty is in the race, too. _____ am working
                 he/him   I/Me

for _____. If you ask _____, _____ would be a good leader
     she/her   I/me   she/her

for _____. Ryan and Patty will speak today. _____ will ask for
     we/us   They/Them

our vote. Then one of _____ will become class president.
                        they/them

Remember The article **a** is used before words that begin with a **consonant sound.** The article **an** is used before words that begin with a **vowel sound.**

Examples This machine cooks <u>an</u> egg in less than <u>a</u> minute.

Think About Read the examples again. Which article would you use before the word **hour?** Why?

_____

Apply Read the sentences. Write **a** or **an** to complete them.

_____ enormous black crow lived in _____ branch at the top of _____ old oak tree. It was July. The crow was hot and thirsty, but there was no water anywhere.

"I'll fly north to _____ cooler place!" decided the crow. And so he did. After flying _____ long, long way, the crow finally spotted _____ house with _____ well. He landed on _____ edge of the well and drank his fill. Then he flew home.

Remember **Adjectives** tell about **nouns. Adverbs** tell about **verbs.** The word **good** is always an **adjective.** The word **well** is usually an **adverb.** It is an adjective only when it means "healthy."

Examples A <u>good</u> dog brings in the paper. It obeys <u>well</u>.

Think About Read the examples again. What kind of word does **good** always describe? What kind of word does **well** usually describe?

_____

Apply Read the sentences. Write **good** or **well** to complete them.

Walter Dean Myers writes very _____ . *The Young Landlords* was so _____ that it won the Coretta Scott King Award. Myers describes children _____ . His characters seem almost real. Their lives don't always go _____ for them. One of Myers's books has a _____ black fairy named Mabel Mae. She helps things turn out _____ .

Remember Some words mean "no." These include **no, not, nothing, none, never,** and **nobody.** Only **one** of these words should be used in a sentence. This is true even when the word **not** is part of a **contraction.**

Example INCORRECT ► There <u>weren't</u> <u>no</u> trees in the park.
    CORRECT ► There <u>weren't</u> any trees in the park.
       There were <u>no</u> trees in the park.

Think About Read the example again. Where is the word **not** in these sentences?

_____

Apply Read the sentences. Rewrite them correctly. Take out every double "no."

1. Ancient people told stories about creatures that nobody hadn't ever seen.

_____

_____

2. These creatures couldn't never be mistaken for real animals.

_____

_____

3. The minotaur was half man and half bull. There wasn't nothing else like it.

_____

_____

4. Dragons guarded piles of gold so that you couldn't never steal them.

_____

_____

5. The sphinx had wings and a woman's head, but it wasn't no woman.

_____

_____

6. You couldn't never guess the answers to its riddles. There weren't none.

_____

_____

◧ REVIEW TIME

- ✔ You use **subject pronouns** as **sentence subjects.** You use **object pronouns** after **action verbs** and words like **to, of, for, by, with,** and **from.**

- ✔ You use **a** before words that begin with a **consonant sound.** You use **an** before words that begin with a **vowel sound.**

- ✔ You use **adjectives** to describe **nouns.** You use **adverbs** to describe **verbs. Good** is an adjective. **Well** is usually an adverb.

- ✔ You use only one word that means "no" in a sentence.

When you proofread, you use special marks.

~~WORDS~~ means "Take out."   ∧ means "Add here."

Use these proofreading marks to correct the story below.

Le Cirque du Soleil is an French-Canadian circus. It is really well. It

never uses no animals. It doesn't have nothing in it except people. Them

perform very good. One act has 13 people riding on one bicycle. I

wouldn't never try that. But they do it good. *Le Cirque du Soleil* means

"Circus of the Sun," which is a unusual name. The circus is a copy of a

ancient Chinese circus. The Chinese didn't have no animals in their

circuses, either. That makes sense to I.

124

WRITING TIME

A **description** tells about something that you have seen, heard, touched, tasted, or smelled. It creates a clear picture with words.

Think of something you'd like to describe—a person, place, animal, or thing. Draw a picture of it on another sheet of paper. Then write sense words to describe it.

SIGHT	SOUND

TOUCH	TASTE	SMELL

Now write your description. Follow these steps.

1. Use scratch paper for your first draft. Write the whole description.
2. Show your writing to a friend. Talk about how to make it better.
3. Revise your description. Take out things you don't like and add new exact words. Use some synonyms and antonyms in your writing.
4. Now proofread your work. Check your spelling, capitalization, punctuation, and the way you used words.
5. When your description is ready, copy it neatly onto a clean sheet of paper.
6. Share your description with the class.

Look at this picture. What do you think is happening here? Write about what you think is happening. Use a separate sheet of paper.

TEST TIME

Directions   Read the KEY WORD. Find the **synonym** for that word. Fill in the circle that has the same letter as your answer.

Sample

answer

A right   C question
B wrong   D solution

Answer Column
S Ⓐ Ⓑ Ⓒ ⬤D

1   quickly

A slowly   C quietly
B hurriedly   D busily

3   final

A first   C best
B tenth   D last

2   dozen

E pound   G twelve
F half   H eggs

4   careful

E cautious   G thoughtless
F reckless   H careless

Answer Column
1 Ⓐ Ⓑ Ⓒ Ⓓ
2 Ⓔ Ⓕ Ⓖ Ⓗ
3 Ⓐ Ⓑ Ⓒ Ⓓ
4 Ⓔ Ⓕ Ⓖ Ⓗ

Directions   Read the KEY WORD. Find the **antonym** for that word. Fill in the circle that has the same letter as your answer.

Sample

thin

A small   C skinny
B fat   D body

Answer Column
S Ⓐ Ⓑ ⬤C Ⓓ

1   dirty

A clean   C messy
B clothes   D room

3   below

A beneath   C under
B above   D beside

2   sharp

E knife   G smart
F rough   H dull

4   same

E different   G similar
F alike   H exact

Answer Column
1 Ⓐ Ⓑ Ⓒ Ⓓ
2 Ⓔ Ⓕ Ⓖ Ⓗ
3 Ⓐ Ⓑ Ⓒ Ⓓ
4 Ⓔ Ⓕ Ⓖ Ⓗ

Go on to the next page.

Sample

A Mr. Baker
B cent the letter
C first class.
D (No mistakes)

Answer Column

S Ⓐ ⬤Ⓑ Ⓒ Ⓓ

1 A No one never
   B listens to Sam
   C when he talks.
   D (No mistakes)

6 E Us can't
   F remember if our
   G bikes are locked.
   H (No mistakes)

2 E Robin sees good
   F with her
   G new glasses.
   H (No mistakes)

7 A Please be careful
   B so you don't brake
   C that window.
   D (No mistakes)

3 A Every Saturday, the
   B Smith family goes
   C to they're cabin.
   D (No mistakes)

8 E An eagle is
   F a very large
   G bird.
   H (No mistakes)

4 E Ginny asked me
   F a difficult
   G question.
   H (No mistakes)

9 A There aren't no
   B more crayons
   C in the box.
   D (No mistakes)

5 A A snake is
   B a animal that
   C can't close its eyes.
   D (No mistakes)

10 E Freddy can
    F ride horses
    G good.
    H (No mistakes)

Answer Column

1 Ⓐ Ⓑ Ⓒ Ⓓ
2 Ⓔ Ⓕ Ⓖ Ⓗ
3 Ⓐ Ⓑ Ⓒ Ⓓ
4 Ⓔ Ⓕ Ⓖ Ⓗ
5 Ⓐ Ⓑ Ⓒ Ⓓ
6 Ⓔ Ⓕ Ⓖ Ⓗ
7 Ⓐ Ⓑ Ⓒ Ⓓ
8 Ⓔ Ⓕ Ⓖ Ⓗ
9 Ⓐ Ⓑ Ⓒ Ⓓ
10 Ⓔ Ⓕ Ⓖ Ⓗ

STOP

WRITING LETTERS

Letters are a way of talking to someone through the mail. You may write to friends to tell them your news. You may want to invite people to something special. Or you may want to thank someone for a gift or for doing something nice.

Think About How many letters do you write? Do you write a lot? Do you write just a few? List three people you have written to.

_____

Letters are a way of talking to someone when it is impossible to talk in person. List two reasons that it might be impossible to talk to someone.

_____

_____

Think about one time when you had to write a letter. What did you have to tell the person?

_____

_____

_____

Sometimes it is possible to talk to someone, but it is better to write that person a letter. Name one reason that it might be better to write a letter.

_____

_____

Letters are useful for a lot of reasons. Knowing how to write them gives you another way to communicate.

129

Remember A **friendly letter** has five parts. The **heading** is the writer's address and the date on which the letter was written. The **greeting** says hello to the person who gets the letter. The **body** is the message of the letter. The **closing** says good-bye. The **signature** is the handwritten name of the writer.

Example

HEADING ▶

301 Pine Drive
Arcata, CA 95521
May 9, 19___

GREETING ▶   Dear Iris,

BODY ▶   What is your new home like? I
                        wish you hadn't moved. Everyone at
                        school misses you a lot.

CLOSING ▶   Your friend,

SIGNATURE ▶   Rita

Think About   Read the example again. Why is it important to include a heading in your letter?

_____

_____

Apply   Read the letter in the example. Then answer these questions.

1. Who is getting the letter? _____

2. Who wrote the letter? _____

3. Where does the writer live? _____

4. When was the letter written? _____

5. Which part of the letter is indented? _____

6. What is the letter about? _____

The **greeting** and the **closing** of a friendly letter begin with a **capital letter.** They are also followed by a **comma.** Capital letters, commas, and other punctuation are also used in the body of letters.

► **Example**

> 92 Benton Lane
> Malvern, AR 72104
> August 20, 19___
>
> Dear Philip,
>
>   This is the best vacation ever. Wait till you see the pictures we took!
>
>   Your friend,
>   *Karen*

► **Think About** Read the example again. List two places commas are used besides the greeting and closing.

_____

► **Apply** Rewrite the letter below correctly. Add commas and capital letters where they belong.

                 9 la playa place
                 mexico city mexico
                 november 4 1991

dear max
    the tree we planted is taller than I am now I wish you could see it

                 your friend
                 Pablo

_____

_____

_____

                 _____

                 _____

                 _____

Remember An **invitation** is a special kind of friendly letter. It asks someone to a party or another special event.

Example

> 6248 Adams St.
> Baytown, TX 77520
> October 20, 19__
>
> Dear Diane,
>
> WHAT ►   Please come to a Halloween party
> WHERE ► at my house, 6248 Adams Street,
> WHEN ►   at 7:30 the night of October 29.
>
>   Your friend,
>
>   *Thomas*

Think About Read the example again. What three things does an invitation always tell?

_____

_____

Apply Complete the invitation below. Write your address and today's date in the heading. Write a friend's name in the greeting. Fill in the missing information. Write the closing and sign your name. Be sure to capitalize and punctuate correctly.

                           _____

                           _____

                           _____

_____

    Please come to _____

It will be held at _____

on _____

See you then!

                           _____

                           _____

Remember A **thank-you note** is another kind of friendly letter. It thanks someone for a gift or for doing something special.

Example

2 Sixth Street
Bangor, ME 04401
July 30, 1991

Dear Aunt Betty,

Thank you for letting me stay at your house for a week. I had a good time, especially when you and I took the dog for walks.

Your nephew,

Brian

Think About Read the example again. What is named in a thank-you note? What is said about it?

_____

_____

Apply Write a thank-you note of your own. Write your address and today's date in the heading. Think of someone who has done something special for you. Write that person's name in the greeting. Write your message in the body of the letter. Write the closing and sign your name.

Remember A letter is folded and put into an **envelope.** The **return address** goes in the upper left corner. This is the name and address of the person who wrote the letter. The **mailing address** goes in the middle. This is the name and address of the person who will get the letter. A **stamp** goes in the upper right corner.

STAMP
▼

▼ RETURN ADDRESS

Example

Liddy Schmidt
5 Corte Palos Verde
Delray Beach, FL 33444

Mr. Jackson Brown
2390 Minnehaha Parkway
Minneapolis, MN 55430

MAILING ADDRESS ▲

Think About Read the example again. Why do you think it's important to write a return address on the envelope?

_____

_____

Apply Address the envelope below. Use your own name and address for the return address. For the mailing address, write this name and address correctly: miss lylah fredericks, 2016 pendar lane, sioux falls, sd 57105.

✔ You write **friendly letters** to people you know. A friendly letter has five parts: **heading, greeting, body, closing,** and **signature.**

✔ You **capitalize** the first word of the **greeting** and **closing.** You also put a **comma** after each one. Then you capitalize and punctuate the rest of the letter as you would for other kinds of writing.

✔ You write different kinds of friendly letters for different purposes. **Invitations** and **thank-you notes** are two kinds of friendly letters.

✔ You send a letter in an **envelope** with a **return address,** a **mailing address,** and a **stamp.**

When you proofread, you use special marks.

≡ means "Make this a capital letter."   ∧ means "Add here."

⊙ means "Add a period."   ⋏ means "Add a comma."

Use these proofreading marks to correct the thank-you letter and envelope below.

293 Somerset rd

somers, NY 10589

february 9 19____

dear erik

Thank you for taking me to the zoo last saturday. i had a good time. The best part was watching the lions and tigers get fed.

your friend

Marshall

Marshall perin

293 somerset road

somers, Ny 10589

Erik Nygren

353 Sycamore ave

somers ny 10589

WRITING TIME

Write a **persuasive** letter to try to get someone to do something. Fill in the chart below to plan your letter. Think about *who* you want to write to and note their *address*. Then tell *what* you'd like them to do and list several reasons *why* they should do this.

Who?	
Address	
What?	
Why?	

Now write your persuasive letter. Follow these steps.

1. Use scratch paper for your first copy. Write the whole letter.

2. Show your writing to a friend. Talk about how to make it better.

3. Revise your letter. Take out things you don't like and add new things.

4. Now proofread your work. Check your spelling, capitalization, and punctuation.

5. When your letter is ready, copy it neatly onto a clean sheet of paper.

6. Address an envelope for your letter. Fold your letter and put it inside the envelope. Seal the envelope, add a stamp, and mail your letter. Look for a reply soon!

>>> TEST TIME

Directions Read each sentence. Decide the best way to complete it. Fill in the circle that has the same letter as your answer.

Sample

You put _____ in the upper right corner of an envelope.

A   a return address

B   a stamp

C   a mailing address

D   a star

Answer Column

S   Ⓐ   🅑   Ⓒ   Ⓓ

---

1   The _____ says hello to the person who gets the letter.

A   closing

B   heading

C   greeting

D   signature

2   A letter that you send to someone who gives you a gift is _____ .

E   a thank-you note

F   an invitation

G   a greeting

H   an envelope

3   A friendly letter has _____ parts.

A   two

B   five

C   nine

D   ten

4   The _____ is the message of the letter.

E   greeting

F   heading

G   closing

H   body

5   The return address goes in the _____ of an envelope.

A   upper left corner

B   upper right corner

C   lower left corner

D   center

6   The correct way to write a closing is _____ .

E   Your Friend,

F   Your friend

G   your friend,

H   Your friend,

Answer Column

1   Ⓐ   Ⓑ   Ⓒ   Ⓓ
2   Ⓔ   Ⓕ   Ⓖ   Ⓗ
3   Ⓐ   Ⓑ   Ⓒ   Ⓓ
4   Ⓔ   Ⓕ   Ⓖ   Ⓗ
5   Ⓐ   Ⓑ   Ⓒ   Ⓓ
6   Ⓔ   Ⓕ   Ⓖ   Ⓗ

WORDS YOU SHOULD KNOW

abbreviation (uh-bree-vee-AY-shun) A short way to write a word, usually ending with a period. Abbreviations for proper nouns begin with a capital letter.

> **Apr.   Tues.   U.S.A.**

action verb (AK-shun VURB) A word that tells about doing something.

> **grin   imagines   went**

address (AD-dres) The house number, street name, city, state, and zip code where a person lives.

> **83 Jackson Street**
> **San Francisco, CA 94109**

adjective (AJ-ik-tiv) A word that describes a noun by telling what kind, how many, or which one.

> **four cones   large crowd**

adverb (AD-vurb) A word that describes an action verb by telling how, when, or where.

> **sat comfortably   go upstairs**

antonyms (AN-tuh-nimz) Words with opposite meanings.

> **bright — dark   smile — frown**

apostrophe (uh-POS-truh-fee) A punctuation mark that takes the place of letters left out of contractions or that makes nouns possessive.

> **can't   Laura's   wolves'**

article (ART-ih-kul) A special adjective that signals a noun follows.

> **a hat   an egg   the year**

body (BOD-ee) The main part of a letter.

capitalize (KAP-ih-tul-eyes) To use a capital letter to begin a word.

> **Patty   Australia   Mets**

closing (KLOH-zing) The part of a letter that says good-bye.

> **Your friend,**

comma (KOM-uh) A punctuation mark that separates things or ideas.

> **May 4, 1991   Yes, I can go.**

common noun (KOM-un NOUN) A word that names *any* person, place, animal, or thing.

> **soldier   park   snake**
> **computers**

comparing form (kum-PAIR-ing FORM) The form of an adjective used to compare two or more nouns.

> **thicker string   smallest room**

138

complete predicate (kum-PLEET PRED-ih-kut) The simple predicate and all the words that tell about it.

> **Len got here at two o'clock.**

complete subject (kum-PLEET SUB-jekt) The simple subject and all the words that tell about it.

> **The small, brown deer ran away.**

compound (KOM-pound) Made up of two or more parts.

compound predicate (KOM-pound PRED-ih-kut) Two or more predicates joined with the word and.

> **This road curves and rises.**

compound sentence (KOM-pound SEN-tuns) Two short sentences joined with the word *and, but,* or *or.*

> **José tried to do his homework, but the room was too noisy.**

compound subject (KOM-pound SUB-jekt) Two or more subjects joined with the word *and.*

> **Ling and Min do the dishes.**

consonant (KON-soh-nunt) All the letters of the alphabet except *a, e, i, o, u,* and sometimes *y.*

contraction (kun-TRAK-shun) Two words combined into one by using an apostrophe to take the place of the letters left out.

> **he'll   wouldn't   we'd**

conversation (kon-vur-SAY-shun) What people say to one another.

date (DAYT) A month, day, and year.

> **July 4, 1776**

declarative sentence (dih-KLAIR-uh-tiv SEN-tuns) A sentence that states or tells something.

> **We went bike riding yesterday.**

direct quotation (dih-REKT kwoh-TAY-shun) The exact words that someone says.

> **Kevin said, "I'll take the bus."**

exclamation point (eks-kluh-MAY-shun POYNT) The punctuation mark used at the end of an exclamation.

> **Watch out for the cars!**

exclamatory sentence (eks-KLAM-uh-tohr-ee SEN-tuns) A sentence that shows surprise or strong feeling.

> **How great this new house is!**

fragment (FRAG-munt) A group of words that is not a complete thought.

> **Amanda and Karl.**

friendly letter (FREND-lee LET-ur) A letter written to someone the writer knows.

future tense (FYOO-chur TENS) A verb form that tells about something that has not yet happened by using the helping verb *will* with the main verb.

> **will see   will buy   will eat**

greeting (GREE-ting) The part near the beginning of a letter that says hello.

> **Dear Albert,   Dear Isabelle,**

heading (HED-ing) The part at the beginning of a letter that gives the writer's address and the date the letter was written.

> **5929 Maywood Road**
> **Bristol, CT 06010**
> **June 16, 1992**

helping verb (HELP-ing VURB) A verb that helps the main verb tell about doing or being.

> <u>am</u> helping   <u>have</u> appeared

homographs (HAHM-uh-grafz) Words that are spelled alike but have different meanings and may sound different.

> **seal — to close tightly**
> **seal — a sea mammal**

homophones (HAHM-uh-fohnz) Words that sound alike but are spelled differently and have different meanings.

> **bored — board   hare — hair**

imperative sentence (im-PAIR-ut-iv SEN-tuns) A sentence that asks or commands someone to do something.

> **Throw away the cardboard.**

indent (in-DEHNT) To start in farther from the left margin.

initial (ee-NISH-ul) The first letter of a name.

> <u>A. J.</u> Edwards

interrogative sentence (in-tuh-ROG-uh-tiv SEN-tuns) A sentence that asks a question.

> **Are you going to watch TV?**

invitation (in-vih-TAY-shun) A friendly letter that asks someone to a special event.

linking verb (LING-king VURB) A verb that connects the subject to words in the predicate.

> **are   was   feels   become**

mailing address (MAYL-ing AD-dres) The name and address of the person who will get a letter.

main idea (MAYN eye-DEE-uh) The most important message in a paragraph.

main verb (MAYN VURB) The most important verb in a sentence.

> **The tape is <u>sticking</u>.**

noun (NOUN) A word that names a person, place, animal, or thing.

> **conductor   city**
> **alligator   gift**

object pronoun (OB-jekt PROH-noun) A pronoun that is used after action verbs and words like *to, of, by, with,* and *from.*

> **me   him   her   us**

paragraph (PAIR-uh-graf) A group of sentences that tells about one main idea. The first word is indented.

past tense (PAST TENS) A verb form that tells about what has already happened.

> **replied   scrubbed   taught**

period (PIR-ee-ud) The punctuation mark used at the end of a declarative or imperative sentence and to set off initials and most abbreviations.

> **Mr. Will H. Borgen works here.**

plural (PLUR-ul) Naming more than one.

> **inches   grapes   buggies**

possessive noun (puh-ZES-iv NOUN) A noun that names who or what has something.

> **Sheila's party   dancers' shoes**

possessive pronoun (puh-ZES-iv PROH-noun) A pronoun that shows who or what has something.

> **your camera   our code**

predicate (PRED-ih-kuht) The part of a sentence that tells what the subject does or is.

> **Helen is studying for the test.**

prefix (PREE-fiks) A letter or group of letters added to the beginning of a word to change its meaning.

> **unripe   rewrite   misbehave**

present tense (PREZ-unt TENS) A verb form that tells about what is happening now or all the time.

> **flow   hatches   buries**

pronoun (PROH-noun) A word that can take the place of a noun.

> **we   you   it   us**

proofread (PROOF-reed) To check written work to change or correct it.

proper noun (PROP-ur NOUN) A word that names a *particular* person, place, animal, or thing.

> **Edward   Korea**
> **Mickey Mouse   Centurion**

punctuation mark (pungk-choo-AY-shun MARK) A mark used to make the meaning of written words clear.

> **. ? ! , ' " "**

question mark (KWES-chun MARK) The punctuation mark used at the end of an interrogative sentence.

> **May I leave now?**

question word (KWES-chun WURD) A word used to make a sentence a question.

> **Who broke the vase?**

quotation marks (kwoh-TAY-shun MARKS) Punctuation marks used before and after someone's exact words in a written conversation.

> **Miss Quan asked, "Is everyone finished?"**

return address (REE-turn AD-dres) The name and address of the person who wrote the letter.

root word (ROOT WURD) The basic form of a word, without any prefixes or suffixes added.

run-on (RUN-on) A group of words that tells more than one complete thought.

> **Harry was late for school he missed gym class.**

sentence (SEN-tuns) A group of words that tells a complete thought.

> **My father went fishing.**

series (SEER-eez) A number of similar things that occur in a row or follow one another in time.

signature (SIG-nuh-chur) The handwritten name of the writer at the end of a letter.

simple predicate (SIM-pul PRED-ih-kuht) The verb or verb phrase that tells what the subject does or is.

> **Travelers <u>filled</u> the airport.**

simple subject (SIM-pul SUB-jekt) The noun or pronoun that the sentence tells about.

> **Most <u>plants</u> need watering.**

singular (SING-yoo-lur) Naming one.

> **inch   grape   buggy**

subject (SUB-jekt) The part of a sentence that tells who or what the sentence is about.

> **The <u>beach</u> was narrow.**

subject pronoun (SUB-jekt PROH-noun) A pronoun that takes the place of a subject.

> **I   you   he   we**

suffix (SUF-iks) A letter or group of letters added at the end of a word to change its meaning.

> **bell<u>ies</u>   slow<u>ly</u>   catch<u>er</u>**

synonyms (SIN-uh-nimz) Words with almost the same meaning.

> **calm — still   ancient — old**

tense (TENS) The way a verb tells when the action happens.

thank-you note (THANGK-yoo NOHT) A friendly letter that thanks someone for a gift or for doing something special.

title (TY-tul) Part of a person's name.

> **Miss Wright   Captain Jolly**

title (TY-tul) The name of a book, story, movie, or other work.

> **"Miami Vice"**
> ***Here Come the Dolphins!***

topic sentence (TOP-ik SEN-tuns) A sentence that states the main idea of a paragraph.

verb (VURB) A word that names what a noun does or is.

> **cures   insisted   became**

verb phrase (VURB FRAYZ) The main verb and any helping verbs.

> **We <u>were</u> laughing.**

vowel (VOW-ul) The letters a, e, i, o, u, and sometimes y.

INDEX